NANOTECHNOLOGY PLAYHOUSE

BUILDING MACHINES FROM ATOMS

Christopher Lampton

Multimedia Demonstration
by Philip Shaddock

Waite Group Press™
Corte Madera, California

Publisher: *Mitchell Waite*
Editorial Director: *Scott Calamar*
Managing Editor: *John Crudo*
Content Editor: *Harry Henderson*
Technical Reviewers: *Chris Peterson, Eric Drexler*
Multimedia Demo: *Philip Shaddock*
Production Director: *Julianne Ososke*
Design and Production: *Rogondino & Associates*
Illustrations: *Carl Yoshihara, Pat Rogondino*
Cover Design: *Michael Rogondino*

Published by Waite Group Press™, 200 Tamal Plaza, Corte Madera, CA 94925.

Waite Group Press is distributed to bookstores and book wholesalers by Publishers Group West, Box 8843, Emeryville, CA 94662, 1-800-788-3123 (in California 1-510-658-3453).

Printed in the United States of America
93 94 95 96 • 10 9 8 7 6 5 4 3 2 1

Lampton, Christopher
Nanotechnology Playhouse : building machines from atoms / Christopher Lampton.
p. cm.
Includes bibliographical references and index.
ISBN: 1-878739-33-6 : $23.95
1. Nanotechnology, I. Title.
T174.7.L36 1993 93–3474
620.4--dc20 CIP

DEDICATION

TO CECILE MCDONALD LAMPTON, who probably would have been disappointed if her son had become a doctor or a lawyer instead of a writer.

ABOUT THE AUTHOR

Christopher Lampton is the author of more than eighty books for readers young and old. These include twenty books on microcomputers and computer programming, including introductory books on BASIC, Pascal, and assembly language programming, and four books on computer graphics and animation programming. He has also written books on topics as diverse as biotechnology, airline safety, underwater archaeology, sound, astronomy, dinosaurs, the origin of the universe, and predicting the course of epidemics. He holds a degree in broadcast communications from the University of Maryland, College Park, and has worked both as a disc jockey and as a producer of television commercials for a Maryland TV station. When he is not writing, programming, or indulging his hobby as a fanatic computer gamer, he serves as Associate Sysop (system operator) of the Game Publishers Forums (GAMPUB) on the CompuServe Information Service. He is also the author of Waite Group Press' *Flights of Fantasy.*

ACKNOWLEDGMENTS

I'd like to extend a heartfelt thanks to several people who helped, deliberately or inadvertantly, in the creation of this book. Mitch Waite and Scott Calamar at Waite Group Press gave me the chance to write a book on a subject I find not only exciting but vitally important; to them I owe this book's very existence. John Crudo, my editor, pushed and prodded at me through colds, headaches, and holidays; without him, I never would have got it written in anything resembling the time frame that Mitch and Scott were expecting (and you probably wouldn't be reading it now). Susan Wiener, as always, helped with illustrations, brought home the milk (and occasionally cookies), and screened phone calls from angry editors while I was trying to read esoteric engineering texts; I promise to lavish the royalties on you, honey, preferably in a tropical country where telephones and Federal Express deliveries have been formally banned. I'd especially like to thank Eric Drexler and Chris Peterson, both for scanning my first draft for technical errors (despite which I'm certain several dozen have survived, purely due to my own ineptness) and for thinking the thoughts and performing the calculations that make it possible to argue about nanotechnology decades before it happens; without them, this book wouldn't have been possible until the twenty-first century. At least.

Special acknowledgements go out to Philip Shaddock, for his tireless work preparing the accompanying multimedia demonstration. He spent uncountable hours researching, designing, and revising the animation to the specifications of numerous reviewers. Thanks to him, and to diligent folks like Lee Kline, who handled model building for the demo, the result really makes this book special.

FOREWORD

Nanotechnology is an exploding field. As I sit down to write this Foreword, I have just returned from the inaugural workshop of Japan's new nanotechnology initiative, a ten-year, $200 million program sponsored by the Ministry of International Trade and Industry. Scientific journals are reporting a growing stream of results in molecular engineering, both the synthesis of large new molecules and early successes in the direct manipulation of atoms on surfaces using mechanical probes.

The direction of progress for this molecular nanotechnology is upward, from the small and simple to the large and complex. We have been on the path to this technology, unaware, for many decades now. We've come a long way, but we have a long way to go. What has changed is our sense of direction, our understanding of where we are and where we can go. Computer simulation has made it possible for the first time in history, to make a detailed exploration of technological domains that are beyond our immediate reach. We can build molecules and molecular machines on computer screens that may not be seen in the real world for many years to come. As a result, we can get a better understanding of our own technological future.

This is important because the changes now in sight present enormous challenges. Molecular manufacturing—the basis of advanced nanotechnology—will do for materials processing what digital electronics did for information processing. Consider what microelectronics has done to the price-performance ratio of calculators and computers. Now imagine a technology that does likewise for everything from bicycles to medical instruments to spacecraft. Our world faces a broad and deep transformation, sweeping up from the foundations of manufacturing through applied technologies to shake the global economy and military balance. The potential benefits and the potential abuses are similar: both are unimaginably vast. The nature of the world we live in will, in large measure, depend on the wisdom of the choices we make.

This book can help build a better understanding of nanotechnology, its potential, and our choices. Its subject is both fun and deadly serious.

—K. Eric Drexler

For continuing information on molecular nanotechnology, please contact:

The Foresight Institute
Box 61058
Palo Alto, CA 94306

The Foresight Institute is a nonprofit educational organization founded in 1986 to promote understanding of molecular nanotechnology.

Dear Reader:

When I first heard the term Nanotechnology I decided Robin Williams had returned in the 90's version of Mork and Mindy (remember na nu na nu?). I was wrong. Nano refers to the size scale that comes after micro ... things that are on the nano scale are 1,000 times smaller than those on the micro scale. That is really small, on the order of where atoms live and breath.

Simply put there is a revolution occurring in building and exploiting tiny devices built from atoms. For example: nano motors smaller than a living cell, pumps the size of bacteria, memory chips a billion times smaller in volume then those made from today's silicon. This last part got me really excited as I imagined an Intel Pentium with 1 gigabyte of memory in a package as small as a caraway seed—it would be possible to sprinkle them on toast! All kidding aside there is a lot of amazing potential to this technology. For example how about a layer of diamond material that grows over a broken bone and makes it stronger than any bone on the planet?

But this is only the tip of the proverbial diamondoid drill. Listening to the soft-spoken promoter of nanotechology, Eric Drexler, head of the Foresight Institute, you begin to see the scope of this new technology. At his recent seminar, the First General Conference on Nanotechnology, I learned:

- By preserving DNA micro engineering can reconstruct extinct species and halt extinction.
- Expect nanotechnology to "patch" wounded nerves and muscles so paraplegics and quadriplegics can hope for full recovery.
- Nanotechnology will allow us to construct tiny, high-powered solar cells that will finally make solar energy efficient.
- Diamonoid could be used to weave a layer under your skin to give you a permanent, and invisible bullet-proof vest!
- Today's garbage will become tomorrow's raw materials from which to build quality cars which anyone can afford.
- Nanomachines will cruise through your body and fight viruses, including AIDS. They will be capable of learning, so when a virus mutates, the nanomachines will, too.

If you have read my ramblings before you know that I feel that books are going to go the way of the buggy whip. In anticipation of that point in time, we at Waite Group Press are striving to build the technology that will replace the book. Therefore, on the inside back cover, you will find a multimedia interactive demo with movies and sound that in about 20 minutes tells you everything you need to know about the subject.

We hope you enjoy the book and the demo and we look forward to hearing your comments. You can fill out and send the Reader Report Card at the back of the book (and get a catalog at the same time so you can learn more about our plans). You can also reach me on CIS as 75146,3515, MCI as mwaite, and usenet as mitch@well.sf.ca.us.

Thanks,

Mitchell Waite

Mitchell Waite

Waite Group Press™

INSTALLING THE MULTIMEDIA DEMO

The accompanying *Nanotechnology Playhouse* disk contains an illuminating multimedia journey, with full Sound Blaster support. You'll explore the size of scale, from the vastness of the Milky Way—about 100,000 light years across, to the size of a nanomachine—about 10 angstroms. You'll watch a nanomachine at work and inspect its nanomechanical components as shown in Figure I-1.

You can immediately install and run the demo by following the directions below. You don't need to read the book first; the demo gives you an "eyewitness" view of nanotechnology.

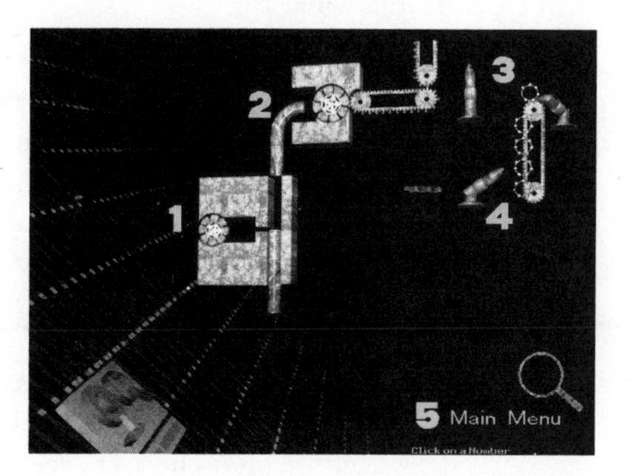

Figure I-1 The Multimedia Demo features a nanomachine and its components.

REQUIREMENTS

To install the files you will need approximately 3MB of free disk space on your hard disk. To run, the demo requires 450K free RAM and a standard VGA or better graphics card. A mouse is optional; the demo detects whether a mouse is connected.

The demo supports Sound Blaster sound boards, as described later in this section.

For best results, run the demo under DOS. It is recommended that you do not run the demo as a Windows DOS application.

INSTALLATION

The demo is distributed on a write-protected disk as a self-extracting archive to be installed on a hard disk drive. This means that the files on the disk are compressed, but the install program will create a new subdirectory on your hard disk, uncompress the files, and install them for you.

To install the demo, place the original disk in drive A or B (whichever is a 5.25" inch drive). Change to that drive by typing:

```
A: (ENTER)
```

(substitute B: if the disk is in your B drive.)

Select a drive with 3 megabytes of disk space free. If that drive is your C, drive then type the following:

```
INSTALL C: (ENTER)
```

The install program sets up a directory on drive C (or the drive you select) called \NANODEMO, copies the demo to that subdirectory and unarchives it. It will then change to that directory and run the demo.

When the demo first runs, you will see a message about sound. If you do not have a true Sound Blaster board installed, ignore the message and press the (ENTER) key. If you do have a true Sound Blaster (not a compatible), follow the instructions for installing the sound driver.

When the demo unarchives to the hard drive, a file called SOUND.BAT is placed in the NANODEMO subdirectory. It provides instructions on how to install the sound driver...although it checks to see if the sound driver is in the default subdirectory first. It'll run without a message if it is.

THE FUN BEGINS

Beginning computer users note that when you run the demo after it's been installed, you'll need to type (from the root directory of the hard disk):

```
CD NANODEMO
```

to get into the subdirectory, and then

```
NANODEMO
```

Your parents, bosses, or advisors may tell you to "Think Big." We hope you will enjoy "Thinking Small" for a change. Enjoy.

Contents

CHAPTER ONE

THINKING SMALL

"Any sufficiently advanced technology is indistinguishable from magic."
— Arthur C. Clarke

The pain was agonizing, but it passed quickly. The pedestrian looked down at his mangled hand, then up at the apologetic face of the driver who had just driven over it. How stupid! the pedestrian thought. I can't believe I tripped and fell into the path of a moving vehicle...

"I'm so sorry!" the driver blurted. "I didn't see you in time to stop! I wish they'd get the road computer fixed. Manual driving is so analog!"

"No big deal," the pedestrian said, sitting up on the curb. The nanomachines in his nervous system had already damped out the pain impulses from his hand. The color in his crushed fingers was already starting to come back.

"When was your last dose of nanoconstructors?" the worried driver asked.

"This morning," the pedestrian said. "I never leave home without taking one. They should finish repairing the damage to my hand in a couple of hours. Of course, there's always the mental anguish to consider. Let me give you the name of my lawyer . . ."

There isn't much difference between technology and magic. The latter is merely technology that we don't understand, as Arthur C. Clarke would be the first to tell you. Remember astronaut Bowman's psychedelic trip to the alien planet at the end of *2001: A Space Odyssey*? As far as Clarke and director Stanley Kubrick were concerned, that was just an everyday stroll around the universe for Bowman's ultra-advanced hosts.

You don't have to take a trip through a stargate to find advanced technology. We've got plenty right here on earth, and there's more of it all the time. And every year that technology looks more and more like magic — *especially* if you don't understand it. How many people know how a computer works? Or a television? Or a magnetic resonance scanner? For most folks, these things might as well be magic.

Magic can be fun, but it's a little frightening to know that your life may depend on it. After all, it's technology that gives us longer and longer lifespans, technology that gets us from place to place at record speeds, technology that provides us with information, music, food, even the bare necessities of survival. There's something a little discomfiting about knowing that our lives and well-being are controlled by something that we don't understand — something that might as well be magic.

What makes modern technology seem so magical? Maybe it's because we view the world on the wrong scale. As human beings, we evolved over the last several million years to perceive the world in a way that helped us use the crude technology of our ancestors. We have no trouble understanding how a stone axe works, or a flint. We understand these things because we can see them. They work on the same scale as our sensory organs. (See Figure 1-1.)

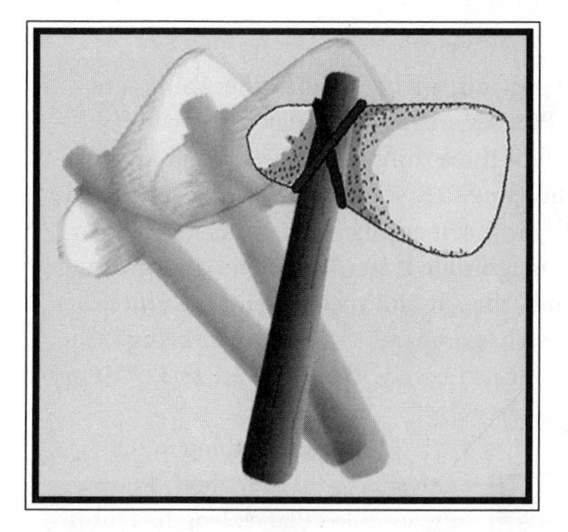

Figure 1-1 A stone axe is friendly technology, as long as you aren't on the receiving end of it. We understand it because it works on the same scale as our senses.

As long as our lives depend on things that we can see and understand, we feel comfortable. But when technology begins to work on a smaller level, it begins to look magical, and we start to distrust it. Our ancestors must have cast a wary eye at the village shaman, who dispensed invisible molecules that cured disease, much as we now look askance at the computer shamans who work with electronic signals too small and too fast for our eyes and minds to follow. We admire these people for their magical knowledge. But we also worry that they might be gaining too much control over our lives.

It isn't absolutely essential that we understand technology. There will always be people willing to understand it for us. But these are the people who will be in control of our lives in the next century. They'll decide how our illnesses are treated, how our food is created, how our energy is generated, how our information is processed. They'll create the weapons of the future as well as the medicines.

It *is* necessary to understand technology, though, if you're going to make intelligent decisions about it — especially if you're worried about where modern technology is leading us. By grasping the magical secrets of modern technology, you can prepare for the problems it will cause as well as the miracles that it will perform. You can make your own decisions about which so-called technological experts are right and which are wrong. You might get rich creating your own start-up company selling that technology to other people. Or maybe you'll just write a book about it.

But if you're going to understand the technology of tomorrow — or, for that matter, the technology of today — you'll need to change the scale on which you look at the world. You can't change the way your eyes work, but you can change the way your brain works.

You can start thinking small.

ORDERS OF MAGNITUDE

Some things, as any four-year-old child will tell you, are big, while other things are small. Elephants are big and ants are small. Houses are big and bricks are small.

Yet when looked at on a larger scale, all of these things — the elephant and the house, the ant and the brick — are about the same size, within a few orders of magnitude. (An order of magnitude is a power of ten. If something is ten times larger than something else, we say that it's one order of magnitude larger.) Compared to the range of sizes that things in this universe *can* occupy, the ant and the elephant are quite close in size indeed. (See Figure 1-2.) If it had eyesight comparable to a human being's, the elephant could probably even see the ant, albeit just barely. But there are lots of things in this universe that it couldn't even begin to see.

Figure 1-2 Could an elephant be the same size as an ant? Looked out on the larger scale, there isn't very much difference in their sizes.

The smallest thing in the universe, as far as anybody knows, is the so-called Planck length. This is the distance over which light travels during the Planck time, the smallest interval of time yet detected. The Planck length is 4×10^{-35} centimeters, which is scientific notation for .00000000000000000000000000000000004 centimeters. Needless to say, that's quite small.

The biggest thing in the universe is the universe itself. We don't know how big that is because we can't see all of it. However, the most distant *visible* objects are about 13 billion light-years away. That's around 10^{18} (or 1 followed by 18 zeros) centimeters — 53 orders of magnitude larger than the Planck distance (and don't forget that each order of magnitude represents a power of ten). It's fair to say, then, that the range of

magnitudes encompassed by our universe is about 53 orders of magnitude. Looked at on that scale, the difference in size between a house and a brick — about two orders of magnitude — isn't much. Even the difference in scale between an ant and an elephant — probably four orders of magnitude at most — is insignificant.

The range of magnitudes that we humans have evolved to deal with in our everyday lives extends approximately from the size of an ant to the radius of the horizon. That's about seven orders of magnitude. (See Figure 1-3.) Any technology that doesn't take place in that range seems mind-boggling to us. We resist understanding it. It seems like magic. Which is too bad, because the most important aspects of our world take place outside of this range, on the *microscale* and the *nanoscale.*

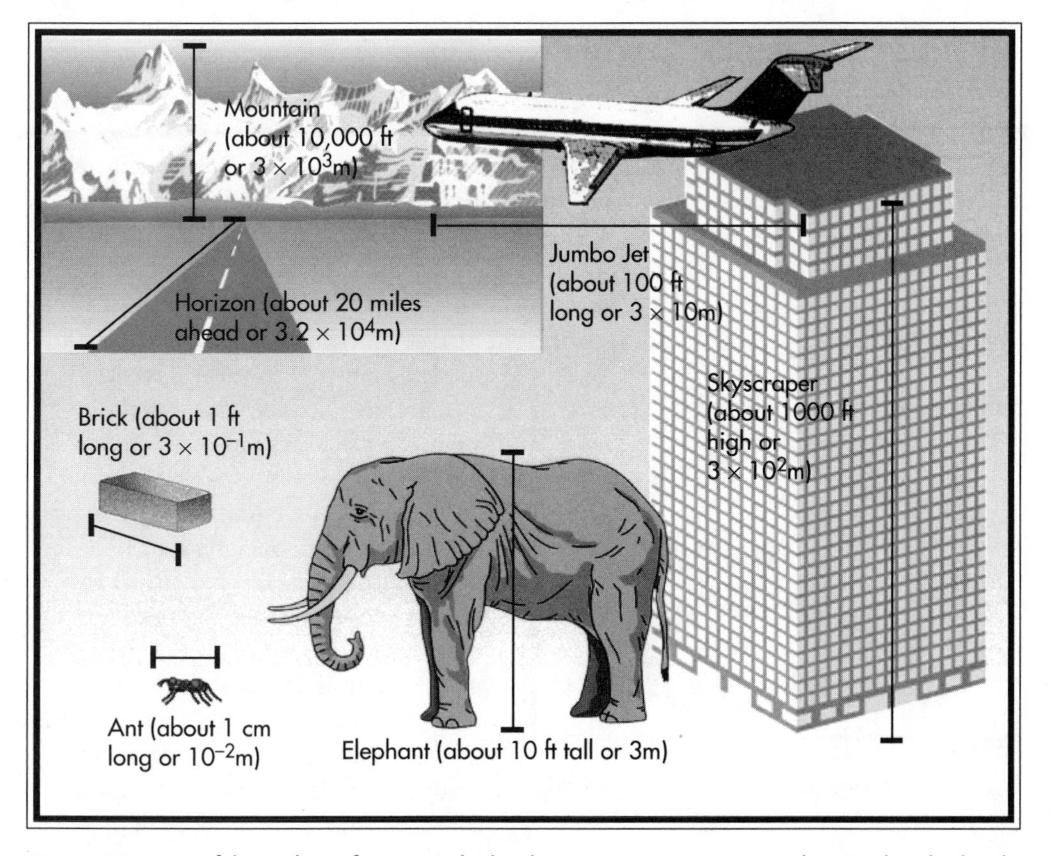

Figure 1-3 Five of the orders of magnitude that human sense organs are designed to deal with.

THE MICROSCALE AND THE NANOSCALE

All living organisms are made up of cells. (See Figure 1-4.) Until about half a billion years ago, living organisms consisted of no more than a single cell. Even today the majority of living organisms, almost all of them too small to see without a microscope, are single celled.

Human beings and most organisms large enough to see are multicellular — that is, they consist of literally billions of cells clustered together to form a single living thing. We can't see these cells with the naked eye; they're much too small. But they're where the real action is in your body. Because they are invisible to us, many people tend to write off cellular activity as magical, something that's much too complicated to understand. The truth is, however, that life is easier to understand on the cellular level than on the level we are accustomed to viewing it from. That's because life on the cellular scale is a lot more like something we've been familiar with all our lives: machines.

It's a cliché to say that the human body is like a machine — and it's not entirely true. Yes, the pumping of the heart and the pneumatic action of the lungs, the swinging of the limbs and the contracting of the muscles, resemble the way in which machines function. But our bodies can do things that machines can't. They can heal when damaged. (Let's see a Toyota Corolla do that!) They change form when an unusual demand is placed on them. (That's how Arnold Schwarzenegger got so large.) They are made up of strange, soft substances that aren't much like the materials that we build machines out of. They can grow. They're even capable of thought.

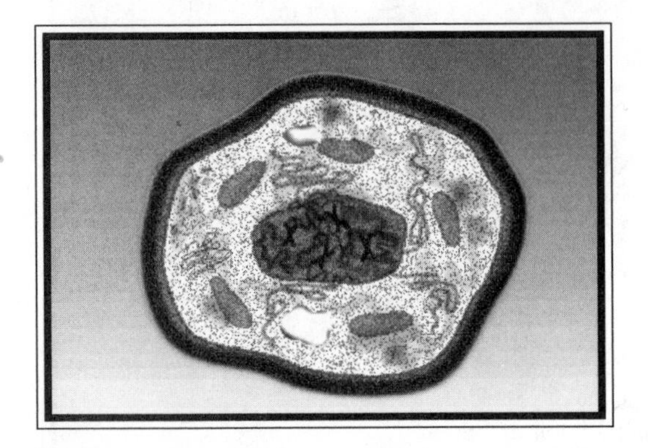

Figure 1-4 A single cell from a human body. Everybody is made up of trillions of these.

It's awfully tempting to say that the human body operates by a kind of magic. And, in fact, this attitude was so common until the beginning of the twentieth century that it was given a name: vitalism. Because the human body doesn't act like other machines, it was assumed that it must operate according to different rules, magical rules. But that's just a problem of scale.

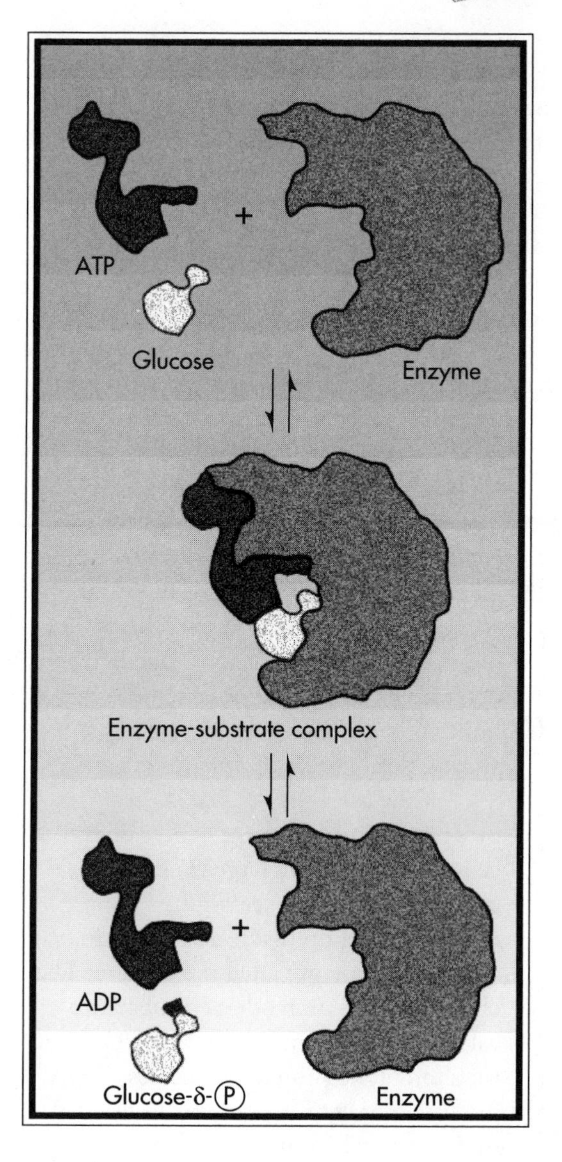

We tend to look at the human body on the scale from which we've evolved to view everything. But the real action in our bodies is going on at a much smaller level, on the scale of the cells.

A typical human cell is about 20 micrometers in diameter. A micrometer is one-millionth of a meter, so a cell is approximately four orders of magnitude smaller than an ant, which is in the centimeter (one-hundredth of a meter) range. It doesn't do us much good to study the cell at the micrometer scale, though, because the real action is going on at the nanometer range.

A nanometer is one-billionth of a meter, so the nanoscale is about three orders of magnitude smaller than the cell itself, which is already pretty small. When we get down to this size range, what we see looks very different from what we see on the human scale. What we see, right here in the heart of the human cell, are machines. (See Figure 1-5.)

Figure 1-5 A machine at work on the nanoscale.

LIFE ON THE NANOSCALE

The nanoscale machines in the cell are precision-engineered to a degree that would amaze even the designers of state-of-the-art computer chips. These cellular machines are actually large molecules — that is, linked groups of atoms. Assembled a few atoms at a time, these molecules perform the tasks that keep the cell (and the body) alive. So small are these machines that you could cram up to 10 billion of them into a cell 20 micrometers in diameter.

The most important of these machines are the *enzymes*, large protein molecules that catalyze chemical reactions within the cell. That means that they can alter other molecules in the cell without being altered themselves. The enzymes are the workhorses of the cell. When the cell needs a task performed, it builds an enzyme to do it.

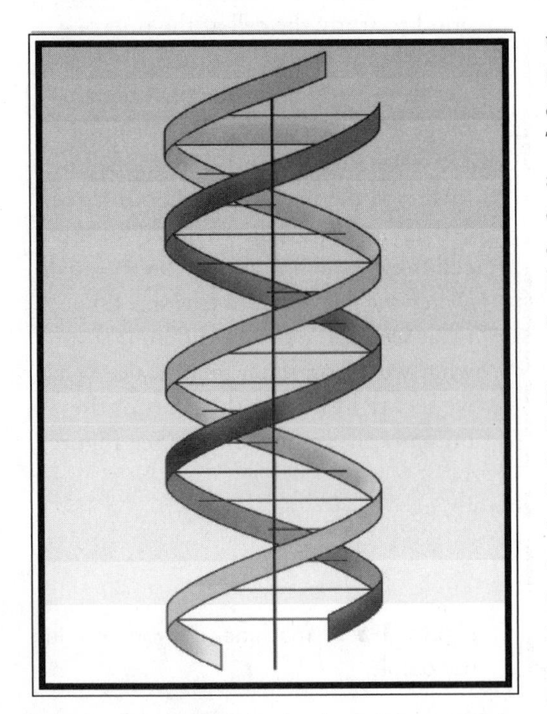

Figure 1-6 A segment of a chromosome, tightly coiled into the structure known as a double helix, shown as a simplified schematic.

Enzymes are created by linking thousands of small protein molecules (called amino acids) together into a chain, like a necklace of molecular beads. There are 20 different kinds of amino acids used to build enzymes. The precise order in which they are put together determines what kind of enzyme is being built. When the chain is complete, it automatically folds up into an enzyme.

How does the cell build these protein machines? In the center of every cell are one or more large molecules called *chromosomes* (see Figure 1-6), usually locked up inside a special protective compartment called the *nucleus.* The chromosomes are made of a substance called de-oxyribonucleic acid, or DNA for short. Like protein molecules, DNA molecules are constructed from smaller molecules, called nucleotides, which can be linked together into any order.

The cell uses DNA molecules to hold information. This information is

contained in the order of the nucleotides. There are four different kinds of nucleotides; they are the letters of the DNA alphabet. What these letters spell are the recipes for building protein molecules. A single chromosome can contain hundreds, or even thousands, of these recipes.

The recipe for a single protein molecule, or a structural subunit of a protein molecule, is called a *gene.* When the cell needs a protein molecule to do an important job, it finds and reads the gene for that molecule and calls on a molecular machine known as a ribosome (which is in turn helped out by a number of other molecules, including enzymes) to build it.

This is what keeps you alive. Although it's a complicated process, it's not a particularly mysterious one — unless you look at it on the wrong scale! The amazing ways in which your body grows, changes, and heals are just the result of a staggeringly large number of molecular machines doing their jobs. The process looks magical because you can't see these machines at work.

Even thought itself results from nanoscale machines making electrical signals flow through cells shaped somewhat like wires, which group together to form a kind of cellular computer. The only part of this process that is still mysterious is why this cellular computer should be aware of its own existence — that is, how it can be conscious. But that's a question for another time.

When looked at on the nanoscale, all living creatures function in pretty much the same manner, by using DNA recipes to construct molecular machines. Plants even use nanoscale processes to trap the energy of sunlight to create the food molecules that we call carbohydrates, thus initiating the so-called food chain, from which most nanoscale machines on earth draw their energy.

Medicine works on the nanoscale. When you take a pill or swallow some foul-tasting potion prescribed by your doctor, you are releasing huge numbers of molecules into your body. These molecules interact with the nanoscale machines that are already in your cells to produce certain desired effects. Many of these molecules occur naturally in plants, where they represent part of the plant's own nanoscale functions. Others were created through chemical processes.

Nonliving things also look a lot different on the nanoscale than they do on the human scale, though they are usually a great deal less complicated than living things. Seemingly mysterious phenomena like texture, color, and hardness are usually the result of how materials are put together on the nanoscale. Hard substances like diamonds are constructed from rigidly bonded lattices of molecules, soft substances like sponges or fabrics from somewhat more forgiving networks of atoms, liquids from molecules that are almost completely disconnected from one another. The mysterious differences between one substance and another aren't mysterious at all on the nanoscale.

NANOTECHNOLOGY

The real action in this world takes place at the nanoscale. Yet human technology traditionally has been constructed on the human scale, the scale that ranges from the centimeter size of an ant to the several-kilometer size of the circle of the horizon. It's natural for humans to build technology on this scale, because this is the scale at which we perceive the world.

But human-scale technology is rapidly approaching its limits. To get beyond those limits, the technology of the late twentieth century is growing ever smaller and smaller. Over a fifty-year period, computers have shrunk from the scale of racks full of vacuum tubes to the scale of postage-stamp-size integrated circuits containing the equivalent of millions of transistors. Molecular biologists have even learned to manipulate the natural nanoscale machines of the cell, albeit in a fairly crude way.

Cutting-edge human technology now works on the microscale, where working parts measure barely more than a micrometer across. In the next century, the technological state-of-the-art will continue getting smaller and smaller, until it reaches the level where the real action is. Inevitably, by the middle of the twenty-first century — and perhaps much, much sooner — human technology will reach the nanoscale. At that point, computer technology and biotechnology will become indistinguishable. They will blend together with other rapidly shrinking technologies to become nanotechnology.

..."An automobile accident?" said the attorney in disbelief. "Get real! Nobody's successfully sued anybody for hitting them with a car in fifty years. You might as well sue this guy for bumping into you in the hallway. Maybe if he'd run over your head, you'd have a case — but then your estate would have to sue."

"Gee," said the pedestrian, glancing once again at his perfectly healed hand. "When I was kid, people sued over automobile accidents all the time."

"When you were a kid," the attorney said, "they didn't even have virtual reality, let alone nanotechnology. And people actu-

ally grew old." He shuddered. "Wrinkles and sagging chins! What a disgusting thought!"

The pedestrian sighed. "Sorry for taking up your time. Er, by the way, how old are you?"

"Thirty-three," the attorney said. "Why?"

"Oh, no reason," the pedestrian told him. As he turned to go, the pedestrian decided that he needed a new lawyer. An older one. Somebody his own age. Maybe a hundred-and-twenty or thereabouts. Sheesh, he hadn't even been born in the same millennium as this pipsqueak.

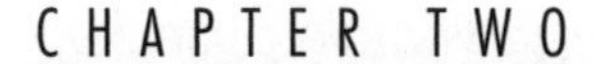
CHAPTER TWO

THE POTENTIAL OF NANO-TECHNOLOGY

The bulldozer operator shifted gears and brought her vehicle to a halt. Directly in front of her sat a hill of dirt blocking the path of the new highway. It must have been left there by the explosives crew who had cleared this area the week before, she thought. She wiped her forehead with a handkerchief and tried to figure out what to do next.

"Looks like nanofood to me," said a nearby man in a hardhat.

"You think so?" the bulldozer operator asked. "Have the chemical guys run an assay on that stuff yet?"

"Yeah," said the man in the hardhat. "It's got all the right atoms in it to build nanostuff. All we need to do is bring in one of those portable molecular manufacturer trucks and shovel the dirt in."

As if on cue, a large vehicle pulled up on the other side of the mound of dirt. The front of the vehicle resembled the cab of a truck, but the rest of it looked more like a small factory. The truck driver hopped out and signaled to the bulldozer operator.

"Looks like the nanotech guys are here already," the bulldozer operator said to the man in the hardhat. "Let's get to work!"

She drove the bulldozer straight into the hill of dirt, pushing a large mound of it toward an open door in the side of the factory-like vehicle. An automatic conveyor built into the vehicle then picked up the dirt and lifted it inside.

"So what are you gonna make this time?" the bulldozer operator asked. "Even after you've made the road surface, there's gonna be a lot of nanofood left to play with!"

"Whatever you need," the truck driver shrugged and said.

"Well," the man in the hardhat said, "I promised my wife I'd bring home some groceries."

"And I could use some new golf clubs," the bulldozer operator said.

"Coming right up," the truck driver said. He punched some buttons set into a panel on the side of the vehicle. A moment later, a brown bag filled with groceries slid out of an opening in the vehicle's rear, along with a golf bag filled with clubs.

"You must want something else," the truck driver said.

The man in the hardhat and the bulldozer operator paused for a moment to think.

"Hurry up!" snapped the truck driver. "At this rate, it'll take us all day to get rid of this dirt!"

"Okay, okay!" the bulldozer operator said in a peevish voice. "But I still haven't had a chance to use all that stuff you made for us last week!"...

Technology on the macroscale — the scale on which human beings normally operate — is sometimes called *bulk technology,* because it moves atoms around by the carload. A

Figure 2-1 Two bulk technologies at work.

bulldozer shoveling a mound of dirt moves more atoms than there are grains of sand on a beach, and the individual specks of dirt fall where they may.

Of course, it hardly matters that a bulldozer doesn't function on the atomic level. It doesn't need to. When a ton of earth has to be scooped out of the road, nobody cares where the individual atoms wind up, even if a few of them spill into places where they don't belong. But not all technologies benefit from bulk. A surgeon's knife, for instance, is designed to cut as precisely through human flesh as is possible, yet it usually ends up destroying cells by the thousands and causing almost as much damage to the patient's bodily tissues as the condition it was intended to cure. (See Figure 2-1.)

Nanotechnology, the technology of nanoscale machines and manufacturing, isn't a bulk technology. It's a molecular technology. This means that it won't be especially efficient at moving mounds of earth. On the other hand, a few million nanomachines turned loose on a ton of dirt might be able to do something even more useful, like transform it into piles of prepackaged food for the homeless. A nanoscale surgeon's knife could slip between the individual cells of the patient's skin and zero in on the disease itself, excising tumors or repairing wounds without damaging anything else in the process. (See Figure 2-2.)

The truth is, there are few limits to what nanotechnology *could* do. What it *will* do is another question, but if it realizes only a tenth of what it has the potential to do, it could change the world in which we live almost beyond recognition.

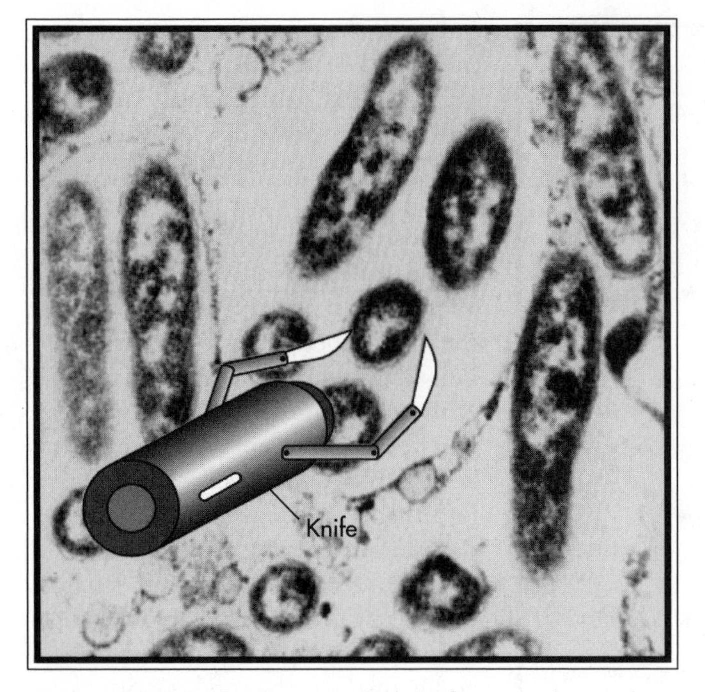

Figure 2-2 A molecular surgeon's knife at work. Painless and worry-free.

THE USES OF SMALLNESS

It's the early twenty-first century. The first nanomachines are rolling off a molecule-sized assembly line. What are we going to do with them?

A better question would be, what *aren't* we going to do with them? Once we have the ability to control atoms, there are few things that can't be controlled or assembled. However, there are three areas in which nanotechnology will prove especially useful: medicine, manufacturing, and computers. In this chapter, we'll take a quick look at how each of these technologies could be affected by nanotechnology.

MOLECULAR MANUFACTURING

Human beings are amazingly adept at building things. It's our particular talent. Cheetahs run faster. Turtles live longer. Dogs have a better sense of smell. But humans build better than anything else on the planet.

Even such well-known builders of the animal world as bees and beavers can't hold a candle to humans in this department. A bee knows how to build one thing, as does a beaver. But we humans can build a million different things.

This is both a blessing and a curse. We build houses in which we can live in comfort and automobiles that transport us almost effortlessly from place to place, yet in the process we destroy the habitats of our fellow earthdwellers and pollute the environment with our unwanted by-products. (See Figure 2-3.)

Today, manufacturing is a bulk technology. When we build things, we are moving atoms in useful ways, but we are moving them in vast numbers. Sometimes those atoms don't do exactly what we want them to do, introducing unavoidable flaws in the manufacturing process or creating pollution.

Enter nanotechnology. If we had the ability to manufacture things one atom at a time, we could build with a precision that would be as close to flawless as human beings may ever get. A ball bearing synthesized on the molecular level would be perfectly round and almost perfectly frictionless. A metal beam built on the nanoscale would contain no hidden fractures and would be stronger than any beam made with bulk technologies. (See Figure 2-4.)

We could build things that simply can't be built by current technologies. Food could be synthesized out of readily available materials. Precooked steaks could roll off the assembly line by the dozens, for manufacturing costs in the pennies, or less.

We could synthesize brand new materials, much as chemists now make plastic, but with vastly greater flexibility and precision. Why make beams out of metal when we can make them out of a substance that's stronger than steel yet lighter than balsa wood? Thin wires could be as strong as cables, yet still conduct electricity.

We could build things on a smaller scale than ever before. Machines could be manufactured with components a few nanometers across, allowing a precision and complexity unlike anything yet known.

All of these things would be built by nanomachines putting atoms together, a few at a time, in precise, preprogrammed ways. In upcoming chapters, we'll take a more detailed look at how these nanomachines would actually perform this molecular manufacturing.

Figure 2-3 The human knack for building things is a mixed blessing.

Figure 2-4 Bulk manufacturing processes are far from perfect.

NANOMEDICINE

Molecular manufacturing will probably be *the* major application for nanotechnology. In theory, nanomachines can build anything — from computer chips to starships. But where nanotechnology will really shine, and where it may have its most astonishing impact on the everyday lives of human beings, is in medicine.

Illness usually takes place on the microscale and the nanoscale. Viruses, for instance, are natural nanomachines that attach themselves to cells and force them to use their protein manufacturing machinery to pump out tiny viruses at the expense of the cell's own metabolic functions. The result is usually a dead cell and thousands of new viruses to perpetuate the process. Retroviruses are even more insidious: they inject their genetic material into the cell's own chromosomes, where it lingers for years or even decades, waiting for the signal to begin reproducing.

What better way to fight a natural nanomachine than with an artificial nanomachine? Molecular devices could enter the cell and do battle with the viruses on their own turf. Of course, this is much like the way in which the body now fights viruses, with antibodies and killer t-cells. But nanomachines could do the job with a speed and efficiency (and fewer side effects) that natural organisms have never achieved. (See Figure 2-5.)

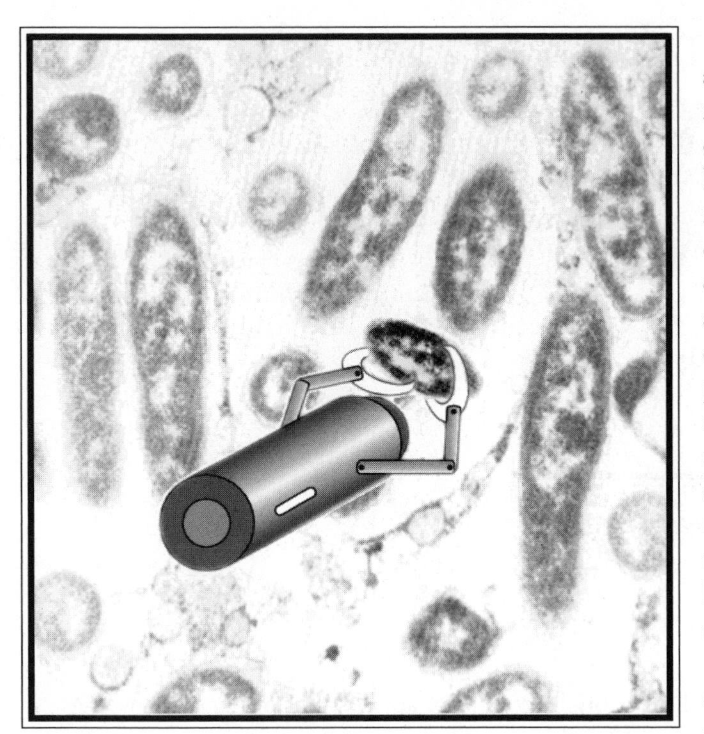

Figure 2-5 A human-made nanomachine goes to war against a virus, one of the most insidious and destructive of natural nanomachines.

Theoretically, there are few diseases that nanotechnology could not cure. Bacteria could easily be routed with nanomachines. Tumors could be painlessly excised, damaged tissue reconstructed. Only brain damage might present a problem: the cells could be regrown, but the information stored by the original cells might be lost forever (unless we find some way to back up the data in the brain, the way a computer user backs up a hard disk).

Perhaps the most exciting application of nanotechnology to medicine is in the treatment of aging. Although it seems like an inevitable consequence of being human, age is almost certainly a reversible process. Once the precise mechanisms of aging are understood on a cellular level, nanomachines could enter the cell and retard or even reverse their progress.

COMPUTERS

Since their invention during World War II, computers have grown progressively smaller and smaller, even as their abilities have increased. Although this process should continue for at least a couple of decades, it inevitably has to end. Conventional processes for manufacturing integrated circuits can only take us so far.

Nanotechnology might take us farther. In fact, it will probably take computers as far down on the size scale as we can hope to go, barring a breakthrough in the manipulation of *sub*atomic particles. Nanocomputer chips, assembled out of individual molecules, would be three or four orders of magnitude smaller than those currently being built, and faster as well.

The earliest nanocomputers might not be electronic computers. Because of the way in which matter behaves on the subatomic level, it is difficult at present to model how electrons will behave in a nanoscale machine. Instead, the first nanocomputer designs will probably be mechanical, working on a system of rods, pistons, and gears not entirely unlike Charles Babbage's Analytical Engine, a mechanical computer that was designed (but never built) in the nineteenth century.

Does this mean that early nanocomputers will be sluggish and unwieldy, like the now-defunct mechanical adding machines? Not at all. Rods and pistons move very quickly on the nanoscale, for the simple reason that they don't have very far to travel. Mechanical nanocomputers will be at least an order of magnitude faster than the speediest of the current generation of computers. *Electronic* nanocomputers will be faster still.

Nanocomputers will probably be the brains behind most nanomachines. Obviously, nanoscale machinery will be much too small for human operators to control directly. The programs for these nanocomputers will be in the form of tiny molecular tapes, not unlike chromosomes, containing instructions that the nanomachines will "read" into their nanomemories. (See Figure 2-6.)

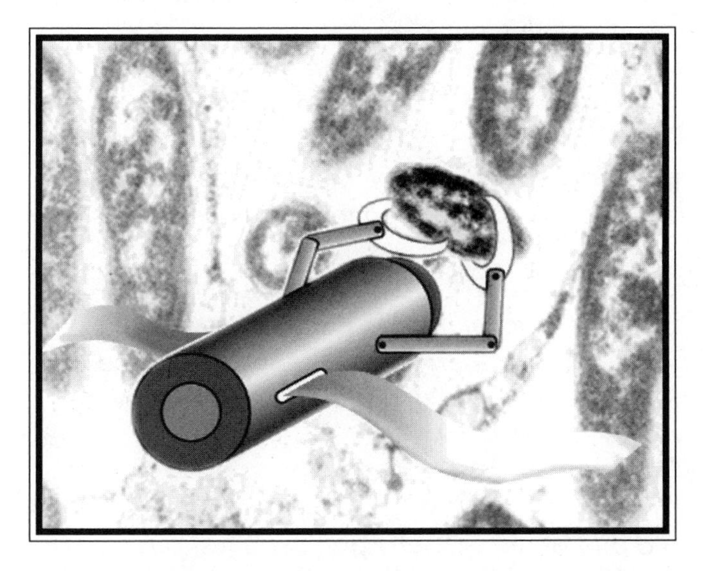

Figure 2-6 A nanomachine reading a molecular tape into its memory, much as a microcomputer reads data from a floppy disk.

UBIQUITOUS NANOTECHNOLOGY

Nanotechnology undoubtedly will have an impact in many other areas, if only because there are few arenas of human life in which manufacturing, medicine, or computers play no role. By the end of the twenty-first century, the only way that a technology-weary individual might be able to *escape* nanotechnology may be to retreat to a distant forest (many of which will still survive a century from now, because paper and lumber will have been replaced by nanotechnologically synthesized materials) and listen to the sound of birds calling in the trees . . .

. . . unaware of the nanomachines swimming silently in her blood, maintaining the health of her cells, and quietly reversing the processes of aging.

...The man in the hardhat looked around glumly. He was surrounded by a sea of manufactured objects that looked as though they had just come off the shelves of a department store. A few were even packaged in brightly colored boxes.

"Well," he said, "we finally finished off that mound of dirt. But what are we gonna do with all this stuff?"

"I don't know," the bulldozer operator said, holding up a shiny new bowling ball. "You want this thing? I've already got a closet full of them at home."

"Nah," the man in the hardhat said. "My wife told me that if I bring home another bowling ball, she's gonna clobber me with it."

"Yeah, my husband said the same thing," the bulldozer operator said. "And what about this other stuff?" She made a sweeping gesture at the objects surrounding her. "I've already got three lawnmowers. And I don't know what I'd do with another television. The kids have five in their bedroom."

"You know what?" the man in the hardhat said.

"What?"

"Next time you find a pile of dirt . . . why don't you just push it off into a corner without telling anybody about it?"

GETTING FROM HERE TO THERE: THE UNIVERSAL ASSEMBLER

In a darkened room, the biologist sat in front of a computer screen and watched the molecules dance.

One, two, three — the molecules began to fall into place, linking into a chain of subunits that slowly assembled itself into a larger molecule. It was only a computer simulation that she was watching. But in the next room, the same molecules were going through the same rapid dance in a large flask. And there it was for real. What she saw on the computer screen was also happening on the molecular level inside that flask — at that very moment.

Her pulse quickened! Would it work this time? She had attempted this same experiment hundreds of times — and each time something had gone wrong. But if it worked, it would be worth all the failures and frustration that she had endured.

Nobel prizes! Millions of dollars in industrial contracts! The first person to construct this particular series of molecules was going to be both famous and rich. And she was determined that that person would be her.

The mass of molecules on the screen had grown quite large and complex, but she had no problem recognizing exactly what was happening. It was working! The molecules were falling together correctly!

She had done it! She had won the race! She was the first person to construct a universal assembler!...

In some ways, we already have nanotechnology. Chemists, for instance, are able to synthesize molecules using standard and well-understood processes. Molecular biologists can create molecular machines using the natural protein-synthesizing equipment of bacterial cells. And physicists have developed instruments that can position atoms with nanometer precision.

Yet all of these processes are either inexact or slow. Chemical reactions are difficult to control with the precision that nanotechnology requires, biotechnology has thus far been restricted to the synthesis of naturally occurring molecular machinery, and the instruments used by physicists are much too slow for practical molecular manufacturing.

How, then, is real nanotechnology to be achieved? Dr. K. Eric Drexler, who coined the term nanotechnology and who (through his Foresight Institute) has been a major force in making scientists and engineers aware of nanotechnology's potential, believes that it will be achieved with the aid of a device called an *assembler.*

THE UNIVERSAL ASSEMBLER

What is an assembler? It is a molecular machine that builds molecular machines. Driven by a nanocomputer and programmed with molecular computer tapes, an assembler will take molecules as raw materials and turn them into useful structures. As

Drexler himself has noted, the assembler will be to matter processing what the computer is to data processing: a generic device that will do whatever it has been programmed to do. That's why Drexler likes to call it the *universal* assembler. Within the limits of physics and chemistry, an assembler will be able to build just about anything.

And how will we build assemblers? Using other assemblers, of course. If assemblers can be instructed to build *anything*, they can surely be instructed to build other assemblers, making them effectively self-replicating, almost like living organisms. If a manufacturing job requires more assemblers than are available to do it, the available assemblers can crank out copies of themselves (and the copies can crank out copies of themselves, and so on) until there *are* enough.

This raises an obvious question. Once we have an assembler, we can build as many assemblers as we need. But how do we build the first assembler?

That's the nanotechnology chicken-and-egg paradox in a nutshell. Once assemblers exist, nanotechnology may take off like a rocket. But getting from here to there won't be so easy.

THE ASSEMBLER BOOTSTRAP PROBLEM

This might be called the assembler bootstrap problem, by analogy to computer bootstrapping. (An unprogrammed computer isn't capable of doing anything, including loading a program. Thus, getting the initial program into the computer is referred to as bootstrapping — or booting, for short. The original derivation of this term is the old expression "pulling yourself up by your own bootstraps.")

Bootstrapping the first assembler presents an interesting problem. Fortunately, there's a solution to it — or, rather, there are several.

The first solution to this problem was suggested on December 31, 1959, almost two full decades before Dr. Drexler conceived the idea of the assembler itself. It was suggested by one of the great visionary thinkers of this century, Nobel-Prize winning physicist Richard Feynman, in a lecture entitled "Plenty of Room at the Bottom." Unfortunately, it was little noted at the time, perhaps because many of the other concepts that eventually became part of nanotechnology were not yet in place.

Feynman's suggestion was simple. We can use large machines to build smaller machines, which in turn can build still smaller machines, which can build even smaller machines. Eventually, we would find ourselves building machines the size of molecules. (See Figure 3-1.) There are neither scientific nor engineering reasons why this could not be done. It would merely take time, ingenuity, and a lot of patience.

Figure 3-1 Big machines could be used to build smaller machines, which could build still smaller machines, ad infinitum.

Nobody ever followed up on Feynman's suggestion. And while it's possible that this is precisely the way in which the first assembler will be built, there are now other routes that we can take.

We noted at the beginning of this chapter that we already have three kinds of nanotechnology, which come to us courtesy of the sciences of chemistry, biology, and physics. Why not use this crude nanotechnology to build the first assemblers? That may well be what happens, but *which* of these crude nanotechnologies should we use? Let's look at each in turn.

BIOLOGY

The nanoscale machinery of living cells has existed, in one form or another, for almost four billion years. Not surprisingly, it includes a natural version of the universal assembler: the ribosome. The program tape for the ribosome is the chromosome.

When a living cell needs a specific protein molecule, enzymes are dispatched to unzip a portion of the chromosome and read the recipe for assembling that molecule. This recipe, written in a molecular language that biologists call the *genetic code,* is copied onto a molecule of a substance called messenger RNA, or mRNA for short, similar in structure to the DNA that makes up the chromosomes themselves. (RNA is short for ribonucleic acid.) (See Figure 3-2.) The mRNA molecule travels from the portion of the cell where the chromosomes reside (which, in the cells of higher organisms, is the nucleus) to the portion where the ribosomes can be found. There, in a process aided by still more enzymes and molecules of transfer RNA (tRNA), the strand of mRNA is drawn through a ribosome like videotape through the playback head of a VCR. As it enters the ribosome, the tRNA molecules attach amino acids to the mRNA, in the sequence specified by the genetic recipe. On the way out, these amino acids are assembled into a protein molecule — a nanoscale object. (See Figure 3-3.)

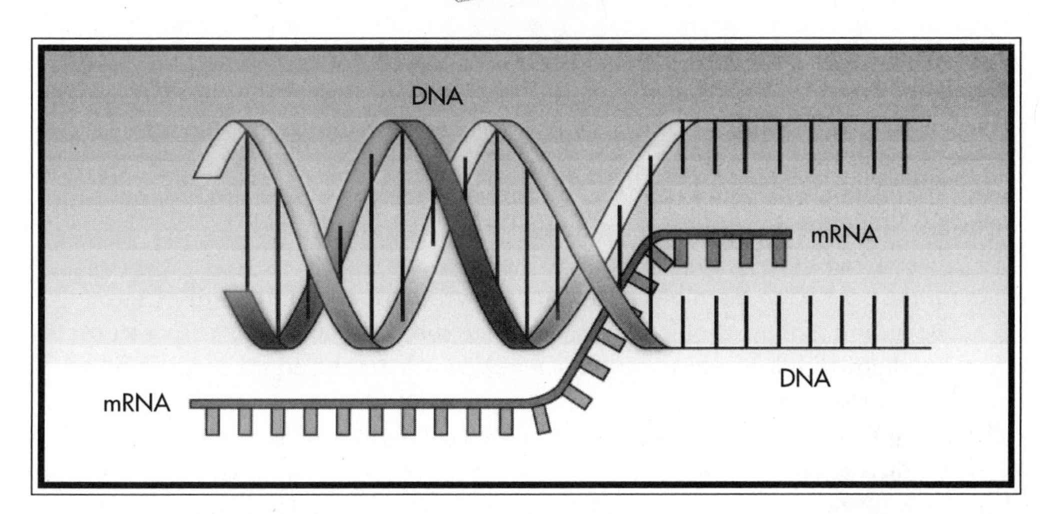

Figure 3-2 Before a protein molecule can be manufactured, the gene for that molecule must be copied onto a strand of messenger RNA.

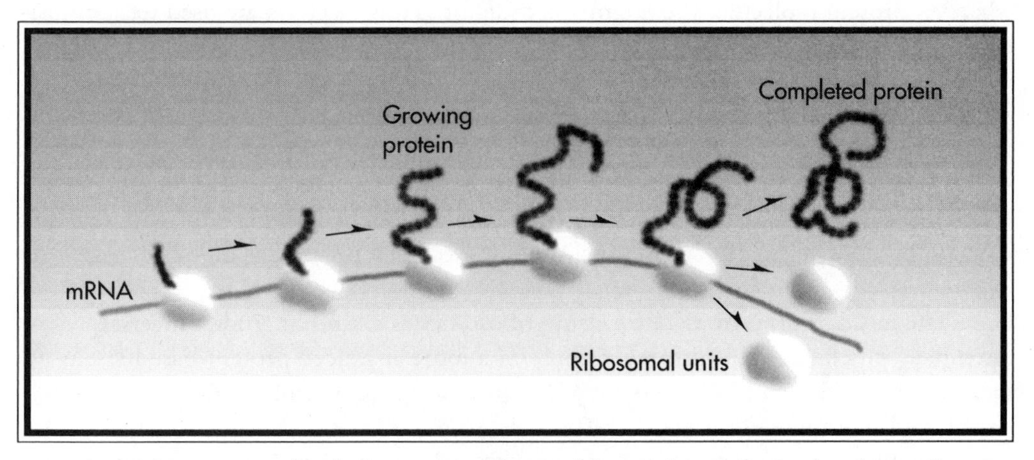

Figure 3-3 A protein molecule being manufactured by a ribosome. As the chain of amino acids is assembled, it automatically folds up into a three-dimensional shape.

Since natural assemblers already exist, it would seem logical to employ them in the task of building the first human-made assemblers. All we have to do is create molecular recipes — genes, in biological parlance — for the parts of a universal assembler, inscribe them onto messenger RNA molecules, and use ribosomes to manufacture them. Then those parts could self-assemble into a larger structure — the assembler — just as do the separately-made parts of natural molecular machinery.

But this "solution" introduces at least two more problems: How do we create genes for the parts of an assembler? And how do we inscribe them into mRNA?

The second of these problems is the easier to solve. In the early 1970s, a set of techniques known collectively as *recombinant DNA* was developed for performing a crude but effective type of genetic engineering. Through the use of a kind of molecular "scissors" known as *restriction enzymes,* DNA molecules can be cut apart at specific locations, then recombined to form new DNA molecules — hence the name recombinant DNA. It's not even necessary that the recombined DNA fragments be from the same kind of organism. Thus, a fragment of DNA from a human cell can be recombined with a chromosome from an intestinal bacterium. (See Figure 3-4.)

Putting human DNA fragments into bacterial chromosomes is particularly useful because the bacteria will happily use their ribosomes to secrete large quantities of whatever protein molecules the fragments code for. Thus, bacteria are used to manufacture nearly unlimited supplies of medically valuable substances, such as human insulin or human growth hormone.

It's not even necessary that the DNA fragment spliced into a bacterium be of natural origin. It could conceivably have been manufactured in the laboratory. Thus, scientists can concoct their own genes, insert them into bacterial chromosomes, and churn out copies of molecular machines that they've designed on paper or with the aid of a computer. The creation of original, human-designed proteins is called *protein engineering.*

The mechanism is in place for using ribosomes as a kind of crude universal assembler, which could in turn build parts for a more advanced protein-based assembler, which could then build parts for a non-protein-based assembler. Are we ready to do this yet? Not quite.

The problem, once again, is twofold. First, no one has yet designed a protein-based assembler. Second, no one is quite sure how to do so.

When a ribosome assembles a protein molecule, that molecule initially takes the form of a long strand of amino acids strung one after another like beads on a necklace. But, even as it flows out of the ribosome, the strand folds up into a complex, three-

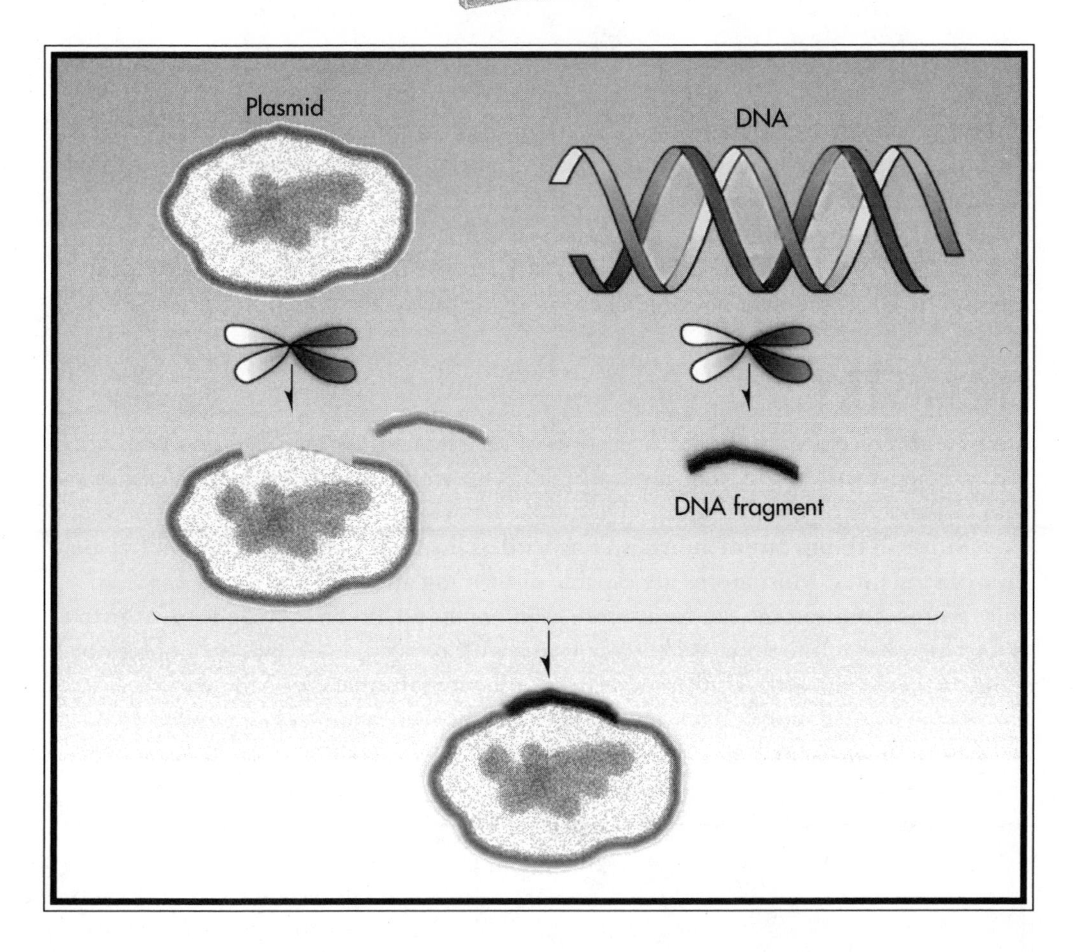

Figure 3-4 Recombinant DNA is a process that allows human genes to be spliced into bacterial genes.

dimensional shape — and the specific shape into which it folds depends on the precise sequence of the amino acids. Although scientists have been studying the way that molecular machines are assembled in the living cell for nearly four decades, the rules by which these protein molecules go from linear strands of amino acids to complex shapes are still not fully understood. This is known in the trade as the *protein folding problem.* Tremendous strides in solving this problem have been made in recent years, but mysteries still remain.

Fortunately, it's not necessary to solve the protein folding problem fully in order to design a protein-based assembler. It's just necessary to solve part of it. We need to know just enough about protein folding to put our own molecules together by trial and error. By trying various combinations to see what they do, we can keep trying until we hit on a design that works. Of course, that's more easily said than done. Amino acids are not the ideal building blocks for human-made nanomachines, and creating a protein-based assembler would be an awkward process at best. Though it quite probably can be done, the first assemblers may be constructed through other processes.

CHEMISTRY

Atoms and molecules are the stock in trade of the chemist. As masons build with bricks and carpenters with wood, the chemist builds with atoms, which certainly qualifies as a kind of nanotechnology.

Building things out of atoms isn't as hard as it sounds, because atoms like to be parts of structures. Most atoms are capable of forming attachments, called *bonds*, to other atoms. Some atoms can form more than one bond, and a few can form as many as four or more at one time. When two atoms with unoccupied bonds encounter one another, they bond with lightning speed, forming a molecule. (See Figure 3-5.)

Once formed, bonds between atoms can be broken again. A large molecule, constructed from many bonded atoms, can break in two. Such a broken molecule can then encounter another broken molecule and bond to form yet another molecule. This process is referred to as a chemical reaction.

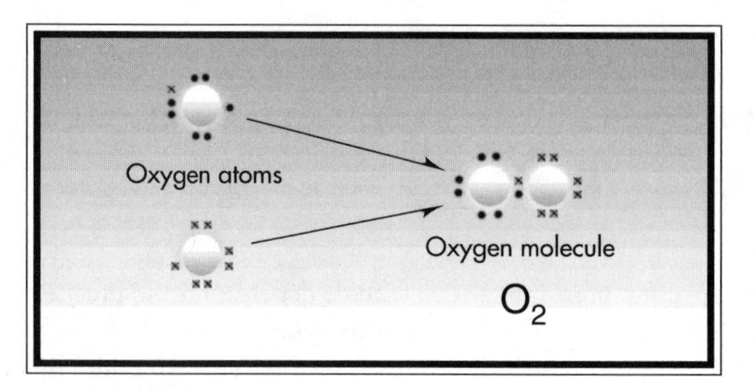

Figure 3-5 A pair of oxygen atoms come together to form an oxygen molecule.

The type of structures that can be built with a given atom depends on how many bonds that atom can form. Carbon, which can form four bonds, is one of the most

versatile of all atoms. Not surprisingly, most of the large and complex molecules associated with living organisms are based on carbon.

As you might guess, the formation of molecular structures through chemical reactions is a haphazard affair. Usually, molecules come together at all angles and form bonds willy-nilly. The process becomes even more haphazard at higher temperatures, when the agitated molecules shatter apart and come back together with increasing abandon.

Chemists attempt to control these processes through devious means. They purify substances so that only certain kinds of molecules are available for bonding. They raise the temperature of a substance at just the right moment so that only desirable reactions will take place. They put together molecules a step at a time, not moving to the next step until most atoms are where they should be in these gradually forming molecules.

This might sound like the ideal way to build an assembler, but that isn't necessarily the case. Nanotechnology requires a precise three-dimensional positioning of molecules, which is beyond the reach of most standard chemical processes. The most sophisticated molecules constructed to date by chemists are in fact the same as the sophisticated molecules being constructed by molecular biologists — protein molecules. Using a process known as the Merrifield method, chemists can synthesize complex protein molecules directly from amino acids, without worrying about chromosomes, ribosomes, or messenger RNA. Once synthesized, these molecules fold up much as they do in a living cell. Clearly, this could be used as an alternate method of creating a protein-based assembler. Alas, it is subject to the same problems as the molecular biology approach to manufacturing such an assembler. For instance, we still need to figure out a sequence of amino acids that will fold up into an assembler — no small challenge.

PHYSICS

Perhaps the most promising approach to date for building nanoscale devices comes from the science that deals with the smallest objects of all — subatomic particles. Although nanotechnology may never function on a size scale *that* small, some of the principles that physicists have learned in studying the basic nature of matter may turn out to be useful in manipulating atoms.

Conventional microscopes cannot "see" individual atoms. In the late 1970s, however, physicists began building devices called *proximal probes* that can create images by moving electrically conducting needles over atoms on an electrically conducting surface. By measuring the precise flow of electricity between the probe and the atoms,

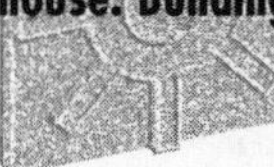

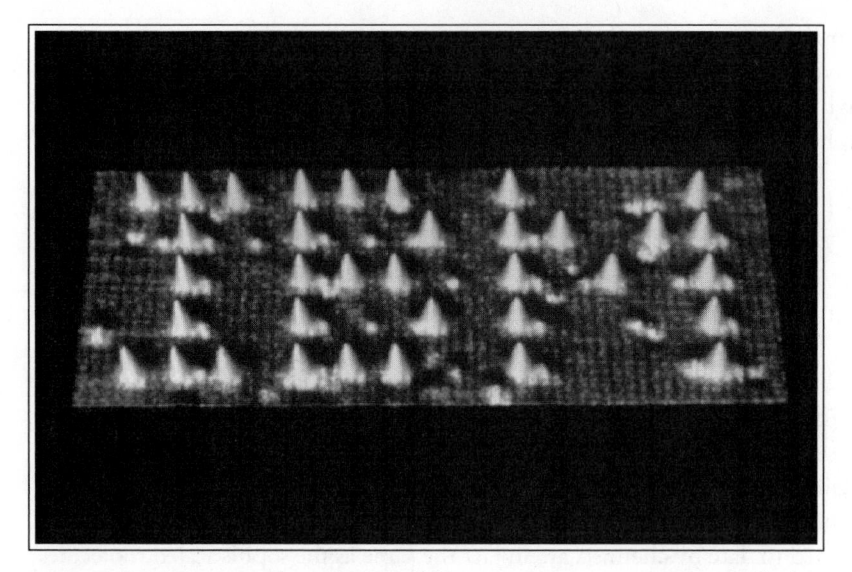

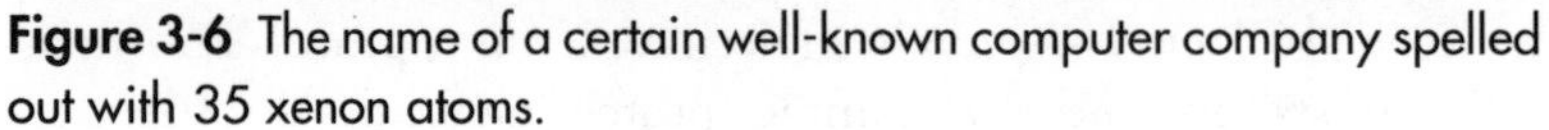

Figure 3-6 The name of a certain well-known computer company spelled out with 35 xenon atoms.

the atomic contours of the surface can be measured with startling precision and an image of the atoms drawn on the screen of a computer. The first popular proximal probe was the so-called *scanning tunnelling microscope,* or STM for short. Another proximal probe, called the *atomic force microscope,* or AFM, works on a similar principle. The advantage of the AFM over the STM is that, while the STM only works with electrically conducting materials, the AFM will work with just about any kind of material.

Both devices are designed to look at atoms, yet they can also be used to move atoms around. Although the first attempts to position atoms via proximal probe produced unencouraging results, recent experiments have been a stunning success. In 1990, in a well-publicized bit of nanomanipulation, researchers at a certain well-known computer company used an STM to position 35 xenon atoms on a nickel crystal surface to spell out the letters "IBM." Photographs of this nanoadvertisement appeared in newspapers and magazines around the world. (See Figure 3-6.)

The process of moving atoms around with proximal probes is quite slow, so an STM or AFM could not itself be used as a universal assembler. But it might well prove possible to build the first assembler using one of these probes.

BUILDING NANOSCALE MACHINES

Whichever process is used to build the first assembler, the result will be the same — a submicroscopically tiny machine that can build anything we can program it to build, within the laws of chemistry and physics. But before we can build an assembler, and before we can program an assembler to build other machines, we must have some grasp of the principles by which such nanoscale machines operate. Will they function in the same way as machines do on the meter scale?

In some ways, they will. But in other ways, nanoscale machines will be quite different from the machines with which we are familiar. Certainly, they will present technical problems unlike any that engineers have yet faced.

In the next chapter, we'll look at some of these problems. And we'll take a close look at the tiny machines that may represent the cutting edge of technology in the opening decades of the twenty-first century.

...Seconds after the biologist realized that she had built the world's first assembler, the door to her office flew open and a colleague stumbled in. "Have I got news for you!" he declared, clearly out of breath. "Have you been listening to the radio?"

"No," she said, a little annoyed. "I've been too busy. Listen, I've got to tell you about my latest experiment."

"Never mind that now," her colleague said, waving his hand at her. "It can't be as important as what I've got to tell you."

"I'd have to disagree with . . ."

"You know Eisenberg?" he said, interrupting her. "The hotshot physicist at MIT?"

"I think so, yes."

"He did it!" her colleague shouted. "With an atomic force microscope! He built the first universal assembler! The press is all over him. There'll be a news conference this evening on all the TV networks. He's already got multimillion-dollar offers coming in from IBM and AT&T!"

He finally noticed the peculiar expression on her face. "So," he said. "What was it you wanted to tell me?"

HOW NANOMACHINES WILL WORK

The enemy waited in the darkness, ready to strike.

The submarine didn't know that the enemy was there, but complex algorithms in the ultraminiaturized electronic equipment that it used for a brain told it that something was wrong. There was a large form lurking in the intracellular fluid somewhere ahead of it. The existence of this form had been reported by the tiny expoloratory modules that it periodically sent out ahead of itself. The exploratory modules didn't have the proper instruments to identify exactly what the form was, but the submarine did. So now it was moving in to the make the final identification.

The dark form seemed to be attached to the outer wall of a liver cell. The submarine extended a long mechanical feeler, with a tiny molecular fragment attached to one end. After a long moment, at least as the submarine reckoned time, the molecular fragment encountered a small molecular structure on the surface of the dark form. An antigen! And it was a foreign one. The dark form was an invader. In fact, unless the submarine missed its algorithmic guess, it was a virus. After another long moment, it found a positive identification for the antigen in its vast database of viral antigens. The virus was a known liver pathogen. It had to be destroyed!

Fortunately, it was a small virus and presented no problem to the submarine. It extended a pair of molecular "scissors" toward the virus at the end of another mechanical extensor.

At that moment another form appeared directly above the submarine. For the first time in its existence, the submarine had been caught off guard. All of its sensing equipment had been occupied with identifying the virus. It had failed to notice an even larger form descending from directly above it. A bacterium! Before it could react, the submarine was absorbed into the interior of the bacterium. It tried to fight back, but its equipment had been effectively rendered useless by the thick bacterial cytoplasm.

The submarine was dead....

What will machines be like on the nanoscale? One way to find out might be to look at natural nanoscale machines, the ones found in the cells of living organisms. But this analogy can be misleading. Although many of the problems that will be encountered by human-made nanomachines have already been solved by nature, there are still quite a few that haven't been.

Natural nanomachines tend to be very simple. Although they can flex, they rarely have anything that could be called moving parts. They bear more resemblance to the simple machines you may have learned about in physics class, or to bottle openers and staple removers, than to automobiles and vacuum cleaners. The vast majority of natural nanomachines take the form of enzymes, which operate largely by virtue of their shapes. A typical enzyme has one or more depressions in its surface known as *active sites.* These active sites are designed so that certain molecules can fit into them in certain ways, like square pegs sliding into square holes. When a molecule or fragment

of a molecule slips into an active site, it will either be broken apart or attached to another molecular fragment. Thus, enzymes can control chemical reactions on the molecular level.

Human-made nanomachines will be a great deal more sophisticated than this. They will have many of the components of meter-scale machines, such as gears and pistons, components that have never occurred in nature. They will bear much more resemblance to the machines with which we are already familiar than do natural nanomachines.

NANOCOMPONENTS

Dr. Drexler and others have already designed some of the components that may be used in human-made nanomachines. Although modeled on meter-scale components, they would be constructed from only a few hundred to a few thousand atoms apiece; in illustrations, they look almost as though they are made out of beads. For instance, Figure 4-1 shows a bearing constructed on the atomic level. It is made from 206 atoms, representing only a few different common types, chosen for their ability to bond into circular structures. Figure 4-2 shows a larger structure, a so-called planetary gear, made from 3,557 atoms.

A large range of components can be constructed from a relatively small number of atoms. And once the basic components of nanomachines have been built, they can be assembled to form larger subsystems, which in turn will be the basis of the nanomachines themselves.

For all of the resemblances of nanomachines to meter-scale machines, there are some important differences. Let's look at a few of them.

FRICTION

When moving parts come together in a machine, tiny imperfections in the surface of one part can rub against similar imperfections in the other part, creating friction. Sometimes this is desirable — if one part is intended to grip the other part, for instance. Gears are deliberately constructed so that just enough friction exists between gears to allow one gear to turn another.

Ultimately, this friction is the result of interatomic interactions: the particles that make up the imperfections are interacting with one another. But friction looks very different when actually viewed on the atomic scale. If no bonding forces are acting

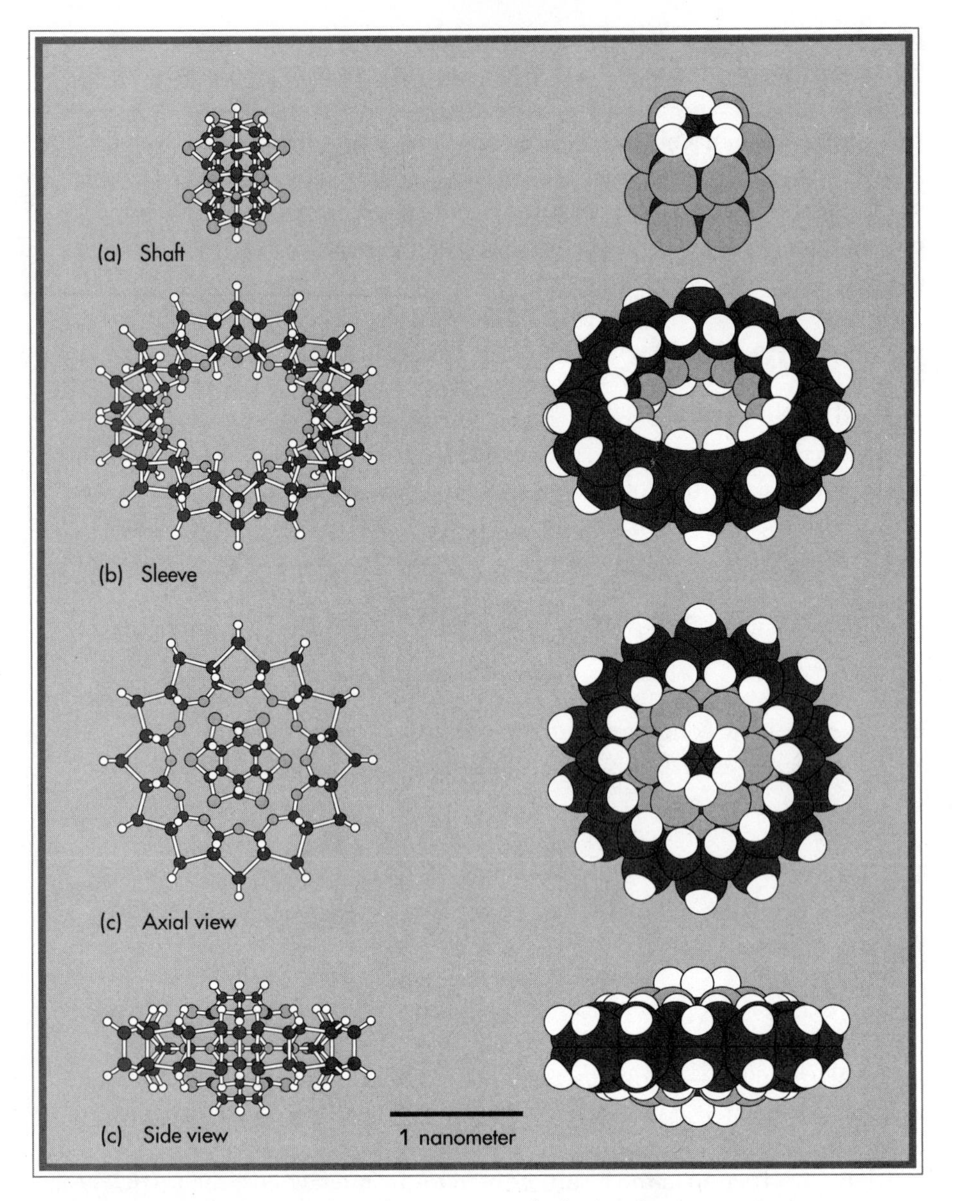

Figure 4-1 An overlap-repulsion bearing. (a) Shaft (b) Sleeve (c) Axial view (d) Side view.

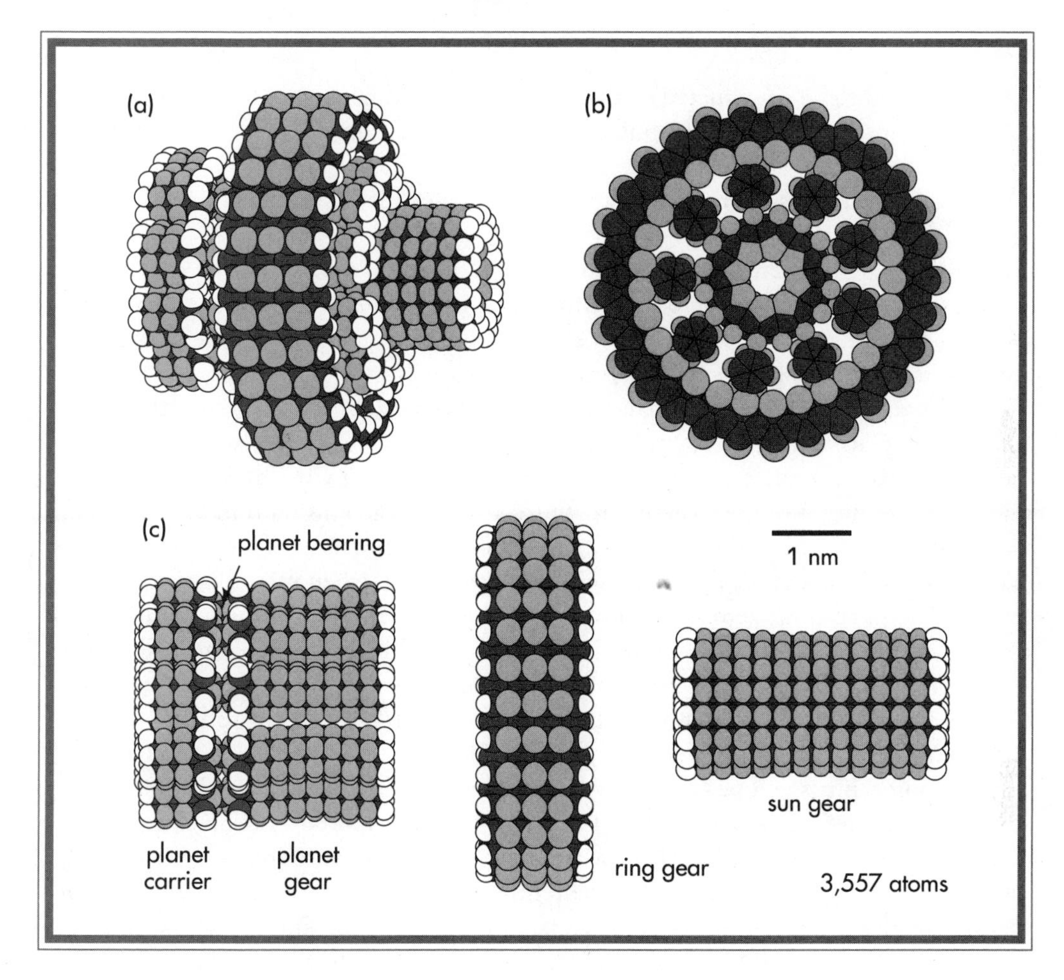

Figure 4-2 A planetary gear.

between two particles or fragments of molecules, they can be designed to slide with little friction, despite the apparent bumpiness of the molecular surfaces. In other instances, two molecular fragments may bond so tightly when they come together that it requires significant force to get them back apart. Just as on the macroscale, this can be desirable in some instances — when you want to pick something up, for instance. In other instances, it will need to be avoided at all costs.

HEAT

Machines need to be constructed so that they don't build up heat. That's an elementary rule of engineering. If a machine builds up too much heat, it could burn itself out the first time it is used.

But heat means something different on the nanoscale than it does on the macroscale. It means vibration.

Human beings detect heat as a kind of sensation. It is a mysterious entity indeed — when looked at on the macroscale. But this is one of those cases where something looks far more mysterious on the macroscale than on the nanoscale. In the world of atoms and molecules, heat is nothing more than a kind of motion.

Like anything else in the universe, atoms and molecules move. Even if they are anchored in place as part of a larger structure, they can move in some way or other, though a fixed molecule can only vibrate in place — unless it vibrates with such force that it pops right out of the structure in which it was fixed. This motion of individual molecules (as opposed to the large-scale motions of the structures of which they are part) is called heat, and it's always present in matter. Even when matter is reduced in temperature to absolute zero — the lowest possible temperature to which matter can be reduced — the laws of physics tell us that a tiny bit of this so-called vibrational motion must remain. (Since absolute zero is the temperature at which the molecular components of matter supposedly stand absolutely still, it's a little surprising to learn that they are moving even then. Yet it is so.)

Nanomachines will be constantly battered by this thermal motion. If they are solidly constructed, they can withstand this, but it is an important design consideration. If nanomachines aren't able to withstand the thermal battering that they are inevitably going to take, they will be useful only at very low temperatures, which means that nanoequipment would need to be constantly refrigerated. This in turn would make nanomachinery far less useful and far more expensive than it could be.

SENSING

Sensing is the ability of a machine to detect objects in its vicinity, either to avoid them or to use them for a specific purpose. This isn't an important part of most meter-scale machinery, because the majority of meter-scale machines have human operators. Since human beings have excellent sensory equipment already built in, it is the operator who usually ends up doing the sensing, guiding the equipment with (usually) unerring accuracy to its goal. Nonetheless, there are exceptions. Fully automated mechanical processes require some sort of sensing equipment in order to do their jobs properly. Automated doors, for instance, use pressure pads or electric eyes to detect a person's presence so that they can open up at the right times and not at inappropriate moments.

The sensing problem is a bit different on the nanoscale. Light-based sensing mechanisms, in particular, will be useless on the level of atoms and molecules, because the wavelengths of visible light are too large to detect atoms and small molecules.

Natural nanoscale machines do their own sensing primarily through a process known as *diffusion*, in which large numbers of molecules bounce off specially shaped surfaces until one happens along that fits. Since things happen very quickly on the nanoscale, it usually isn't very long — no more than a scant fraction of a second — before a perfect fit is found.

Diffusion is a clumsy and inexact process, but a form of diffusion will probably be the best method available for nanoscale sensing. We'll talk more about this in a moment, when we describe the sorting rotor that may be used in nanoassemblers.

THE UNIVERSAL ASSEMBLER

With those precautions in mind, let's look at a possible structure for a universal assembler — the nanomachine that builds other nanomachines. An assembler will take raw materials — fragments of molecules — and put them together to form molecular machines. To understand how such an assembler might work, we'll need to follow this process from the raw materials to the finished product.

In the living cell, the raw materials of natural nanomachines float around in a fluid environment, bumping into one another until they come in contact with molecules of transfer RNA, which bring these loose molecules together at the ribosome to form protein molecules. In a sense, this is a sorting process; the tRNA sorts through large numbers of unneeded materials to find the ones that *are* needed.

That wouldn't be a bad way to start the nanoassembler process. The raw materials of nanomachines could be dissolved in liquid, so that large quantities of all the different materials could be constantly available to an assembler floating in that liquid. Some method of sorting out and organizing the desired raw materials is then needed.

Sorting Rotors

One method suggested by nanotech pioneers is the *sorting rotor.* (See Figure 4-3.) Such a rotor would consist of a wheel surrounded by molecular spokes, with each spoke terminating in a molecule designed in such a way that it will bond with a particular type of raw molecular building block — and *only* with that type of raw molecular building block. (This is a form of diffusion, the process we described a moment ago.) Several of these rotors could be placed at the entrances to an otherwise hermetically sealed assembler mechanism. When rotated, each rotor would sort out its specific type of molecule from the surrounding fluid, releasing these molecules into a passageway inside the assembler mechanism. Since assemblers are designed to build many different molecular devices, sorting rotors for a few dozen different "feedstock" molecules could be placed around the perimeter of the assembler, but only the rotors for those molecules actually needed in the current assembly would be turned on.

This takes care of the first stage of the sensing operation. The sorting rotor "senses" the desired molecules in the surrounding liquid medium, forcing them into predesigned channels so that the machinery performing the actual assembly process will be able to rely on far less exacting processes to determine which molecule is which.

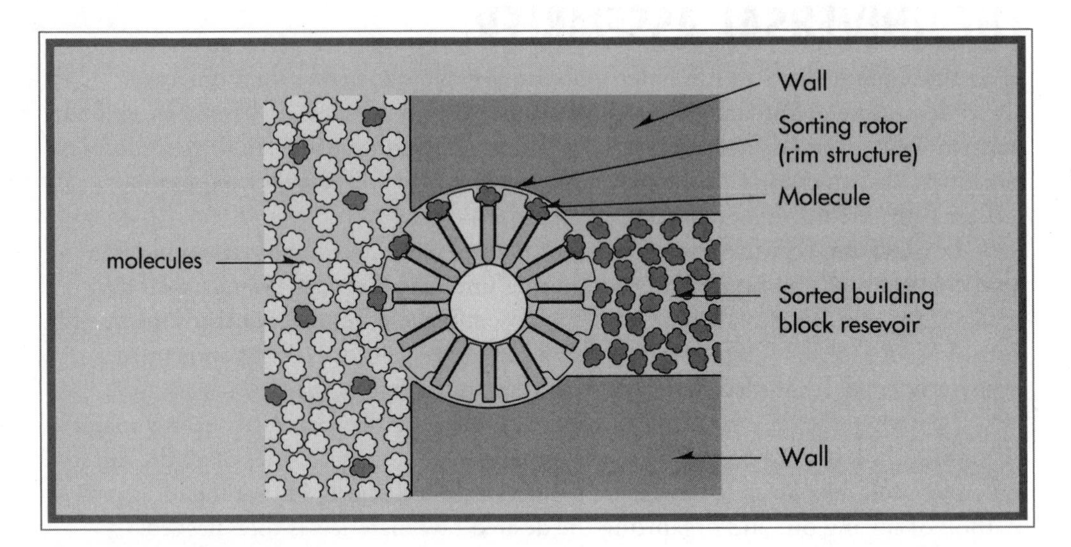

Figure 4-3 A sorting rotor at work.

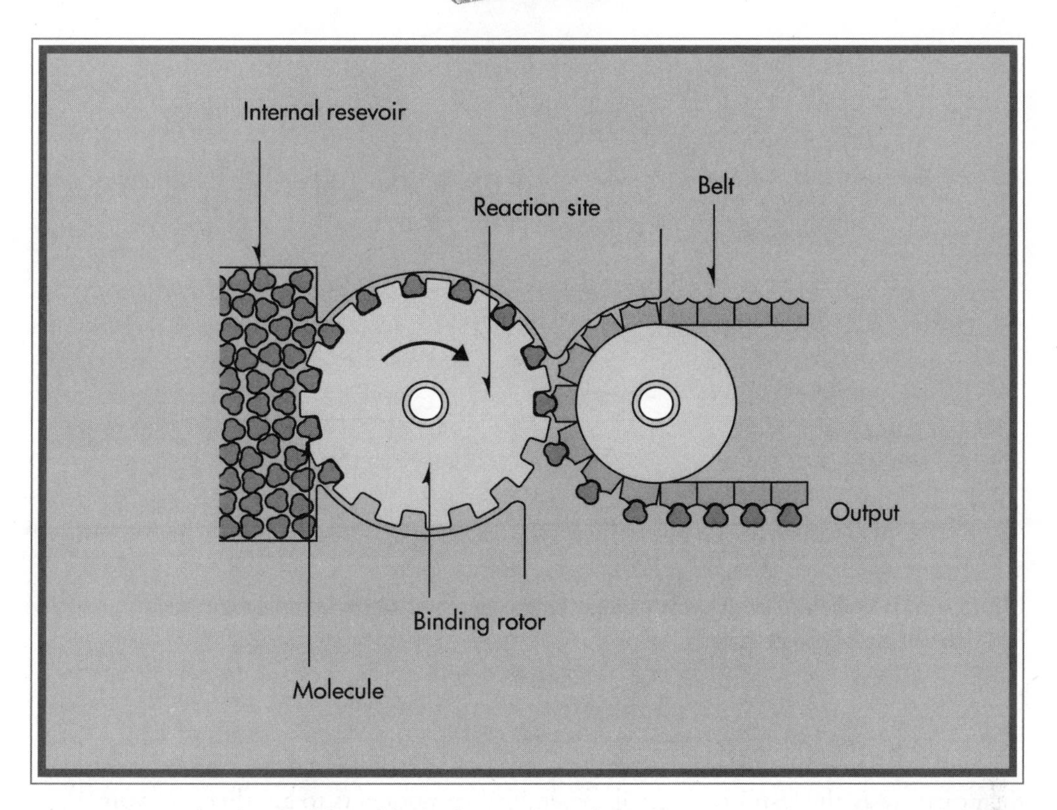

Figure 4-4 Molecular building blocks being moved from a storage reservoir to a moving conveyor belt.

Onto the Molecular Conveyor Belt

Once past the rotor, the molecular building blocks would be funneled into internal "reservoirs" inside the assembler mechanism that will serve as molecular storerooms. From this point on, the assembler bears more than a passing resemblance to a meter-scale assembly line. When the molecules in a reservoir are needed, they will be removed from the reservoir and put on a moving molecular conveyor belt. (See Figure 4-4.) The molecules can actually be bonded to the belt to keep them from drifting off and jamming the machinery of the assembler as the belt twists and turns.

To build machine components out of these molecular building blocks, two or more of these belts could be brought together in such a way that the molecules on one

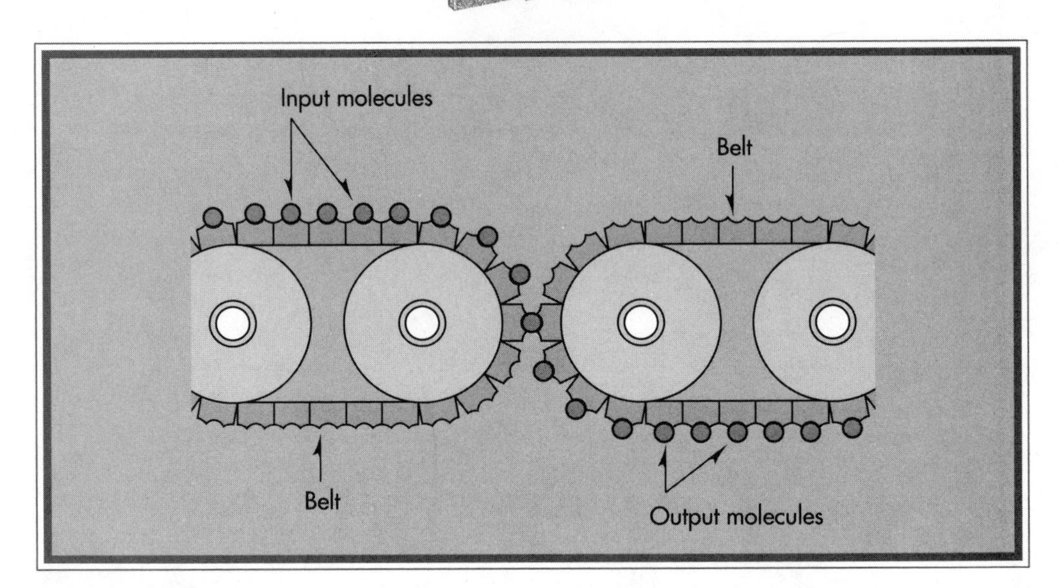

Figure 4-5 Two molecular conveyor belts coming together to bond molecular building blocks into nanomachine components.

belt will bond with the molecules on the other belt. (See Figure 4-5.) The belts could then carry away the resulting partially assembled components to another reservoir, where the process can be repeated as often as necessary until a complete component has been assembled.

Molecular Manipulators

Now it's time to put these components together into a molecular machine. This process will require somewhat more exacting control than the assembly of the individual components. On the macroscale, this is the point when human beings would step in to solder the last few components together. Humans not being available, we'll need instead to do what a few cutting edge meter-scale factories have done — use robots.

More precisely, we'll use a robot arm, called a *molecular manipulator.* Figure 4-6 shows a possible structure for such a robot arm. Note that it's capable of being rotated into a number of different positions, yet it is stiff enough to be positioned with great precision.

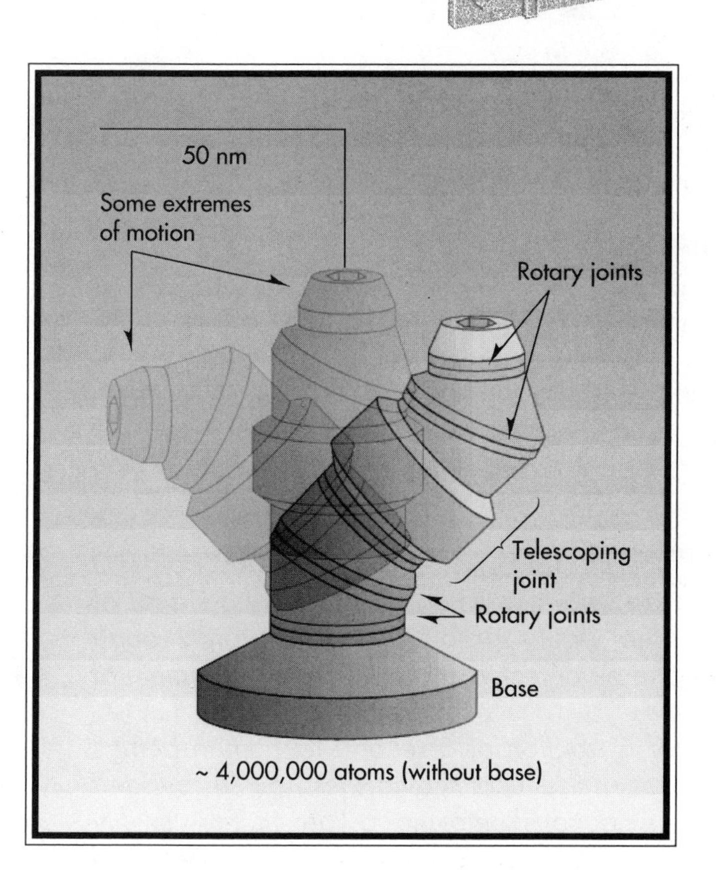

Figure 4-6 A possible structure for a molecular manipulator.

At the end of the molecular manipulator is a socket into which can be plugged any of a number of molecular tips. Like the tips on the spokes of the sorting rotors, these tips would "recognize" specific molecules and bond with them. This provides the molecular manipulator not only with a means of sensing the right molecules, but a means of picking them up in the proper orientation.

The molecular manipulator can then be used to place these molecular components one at a time in a larger structure, building a molecular machine out of the components assembled during the earlier stages of the process. And that, roughly speaking, is what an assembler will do. Of course, we've simplified the process greatly. But until an assembler has actually been built, it may not be possible to describe such

machines with too much precision, since only the actual advent of nanotechnology will tell us what such devices will really be like. On the other hand, it may be possible to use advanced computer modeling programs to come up with a fairly detailed design for an assembler even before we are able to build one.

Who Guides the Assembler?

As we've seen, nanomachines will be too small to allow them to be controlled directly by human operators (though a form of indirect chemical control is possible). So computers will need to step in where human beings are unable to tread.

Nanocomputers will thus be of the utmost importance — and will themselves bring about a revolution in computing comparable to the invention of the transistor. But what will these nanocomputers be like? How will they work?

That's what we'll look at in the next chapter.

...The submarine's death did not go unavenged. Just before it was absorbed by the bacterium, it released a warning signal of sorts — tiny molecules that would spread outward rapidly through the intracellular fluid and be detected by the sensing equipment of other nearby submarines.

Within moments (or a fraction of a second as human beings reckon time), several dozen identical submarines had surrounded the bacterium and were cautiously moving toward it. They swiftly identified it as a pathogen. Before it could absorb them as it had the first submarine, they used their molecular scissors to render the bacterium harmless.

The first submarine had already been partially dismantled by the bacterium and could not be revived. But its death was hardly meaningless. With its final action, it had engineered the destruction of a pathogenic bacterium.

Which, after all, had been its job.

CHAPTER FIVE

NANOCOMPUTERS

The defending army was waiting at the gates of the castle. The Chosen One could see them from the rocky promontory where he crouched high overhead. There were at least five legions of orcs, ten legions of goblins, and another ten legions of kobolds. All there for but a single reason: to prevent a certain iron-thewed hero with a magic sword from getting inside.

This is too easy, the Chosen One thought, holding his enchanted weapon aloft and watching it glisten in the sunlight. It'll take more than a few legions of monsters to stop me from getting into that castle.

"Excuse me, o Chosen One?" said his faithful elvish companion, Crudo the Impish. "Were you planning to attack any time soon?"

"Hmm?" said the Chosen One, glancing at Crudo's green skin and pointed ears. "Pretty soon, I guess. What's the rush?"

"The Princess Drosophila is due to marry Calamar, Lord of Darkness, this afternoon," he said. "I assumed you'd want to arrive before this event occurs."

"Oh, right," the Chosen One said. "I'd forgotten about the princess. How many points do I lose if I don't rescue her in time?"

"Points, your lordship?"

"Yeah, I guess you wouldn't know anything about that," the Chosen One said. "You're just an artificial intelligence." He opened a small compartment at the hilt of his sword. Inside was a large red button. "Excuse me," the Chosen One said, pressing the button. "I've gotta go."

For a brief instant, Crudo stared at his master in confusion. Then he simply vanished. The Chosen One reached up to his head and pulled off the sleek black helmet that had abruptly appeared there. Underneath was the face of a 12-year-old boy.

"Well," said the salesman. "How did you like it? Quite an experience, eh? The Mark 74 Virtual Reality unit uses the latest in three-dimensional nanoprocessors. It can maintain 2,000 simultaneous artificial intelligences, all with an average IQ of 160, and can output 60 frames per second of ultra-high-resolution 3D graphics directly to the visual cortex of your brain. Not to mention full sound, smell, and touchstim. And as part of our special introductory offer, it comes with a built-in cartridge containing Tolkien's entire Middle Earth, complete with all the characters from his novels!"

"Nah," said the 12-year-old Chosen One, whose attention had already wandered to a nearby rack of interactive comic books. "My parents bought me one of those last year. What have you got that's really neat?"...

Computers are at once the simplest and most complicated inventions of twentieth-century technology: simple because they are made from building blocks called *logic gates* that each perform a single task, complicated because those building blocks can be put together in a mind-boggling number of different ways. And even after they are put together, these incredible machines can be effectively "rewired" through a marvelous invention called *software* that allows a single machine to become a nearly infinite variety of machines.

A computer is nothing more (or less) than a device for taking one or more information-bearing signals and converting them into different signals, according to a predefined sequence of steps called a *program*. Described in such stripped-down terms, that may seem like an almost trivial process, but consider that those signals can carry just about any kind of information imaginable, given the right program and a way to input and output the data. For instance, the signal can be music, visual images, the hum of a modem over a telephone line, or the tapping of fingertips on a keyboard. And any one of these data types can be converted into any of the others. Hence, a computer can (potentially, at least) become a musical instrument, an artist's easel, a typewriter, or a television. Further, it can do the jobs of any of these more traditional instruments in ways that would have been impossible in an earlier age. A computerized typewriter (usually referred to as a word processor) can edit text seamlessly, search through multiple documents for a word or phrase, even correct the typist's spelling. Try that on your antique Smith-Corona!

LOGIC GATES

At the heart of each and every one of these magical instruments is the logic gate — or, more properly, several million logic gates. A logic gate is an electronic circuit that makes decisions. One or more signals go into the gate, a single signal comes out. The signal that comes out is determined by the signals that go in. In effect, the gate "decides" what signals will be output based on what signals are input.

This isn't all that complicated a process. Before this chapter is out, we'll show you how to construct a logic gate from parts that you may actually have around the house. Eric Drexler has suggested that extremely tiny logic gates can be put together from components no larger than a few atoms apiece. These nanologic gates could form the basis for the nanocomputers that will make nanotechnology feasible.

Almost all modern microcomputers are electronic. That means that the signals entering and leaving the logic gates consist of streams of electrons surging at close to the speed of light down wires or etched circuits. But the signal doesn't have to be electronic; it can consist of rays of light, moving pistons, even smoke signals, provided that there exists some process by which these signals can be channeled through a series of logic gates.

The actual signal entering a logic gate takes the form of a binary number. Once again, this is more a matter of convention than necessity. The signal could also take the form of a decimal number, the kind that we ordinarily count with, but that would introduce unnecessary complications into the process. Although binary numbers might seem strange to us at first blush, after a lifetime of counting in decimal, they are

extremely simple to process. This, in turn, makes the workings of a logic gate surprisingly easy to understand.

A binary number is a number made up of the digits 0 and 1 — and *only* the digits 0 and 1. Any number that can be represented in decimal (which is to say, any whole number, if not all possible fractions) can also be represented in binary, though it will usually require more digits to do so. For instance, the three-digit decimal number 999 expands in binary to the ten-digit number 1111100111.

Logic gates process binary numbers a single digit at a time. Thus, each of the input signals to a logic gate consists of either the digit 0 or the digit 1. In electronic computers, 0 is usually represented by a low-voltage electric current, while 1 is represented by a high-voltage electric current. (This can be done the other way around as well, as long as the computer designer is consistent about it.)

AND GATES

There's no better way to learn what logic gates do than to watch one in action, metaphorically speaking. We'll arbitrarily examine the type of logic gate referred to as an AND gate, a name that neatly represents the logical nature of the decisions that the gate is called upon to make.

Figure 5-1 represents an AND gate schematically. (The shape of the gate itself is based on the conventions used in electronic wiring diagrams, and isn't necessarily the actual shape that such a circuit would take.) Entering the left side of the gate are two input signals, which we'll call A and B. Each of these signals can take two values, 0 and 1. The form that the signal takes — electronic, mechanical, whatever — doesn't matter, as long as the gate has been constructed to recognize that form and process it accordingly. Exiting the right side of the gate is a single output signal, which we'll call C. Like A and B, it can also take the two values 0 and 1.

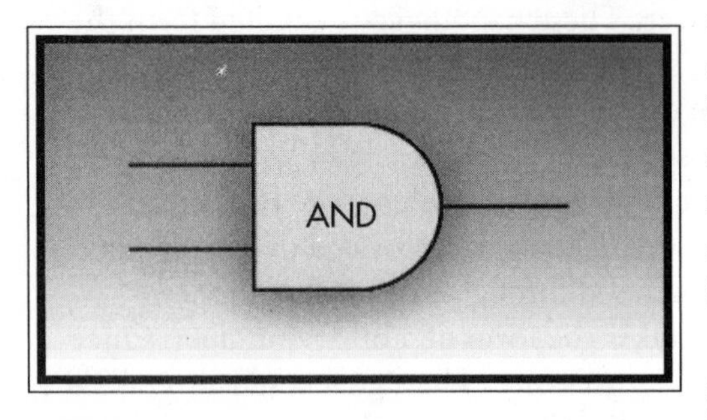

Figure 5-1 Schematic representation of an AND gate.

When the input signals enter the gate through A and B, they are compared by the circuitry inside the gate. If both signals are 1s, the gate outputs a value of 1; otherwise, it outputs a 0. It's convenient here to think of the 1 signal as representing the concept of "true," and the Ø signal as representing the concept of "false." Thus, the input to the AND gate is equivalent to a sentence along the lines of, "I am a Presbyterian AND I weigh 180 pounds." Only if both halves of this sentence are true (1) can the whole sentence be regarded as true. If either half is false (0), then the whole sentence is false. In the same way, the output signal of the AND gate is true (1) only if both input signals are true; otherwise, it is false (0).

OR, NOT, AND NAND GATES

The AND gate itself might be little more than a mildly diverting novelty if it weren't for the fact that it can be combined with other logic gates to perform vastly more sophisticated tasks. Two other logic gates with which AND gates are commonly combined are the OR and NOT gates. Once again, these gates perform logical tasks not unlike the equivalent English words, given that 1 is regarded as representing the concept of "true" and 0 the concept of "false." For instance, the OR gate (shown in Figure 5-2) outputs a 1 (true) if one OR both of its two inputs are true; it only outputs a 0 (false) if both inputs are false. This is analogous to the English sentence, "Either I'm seeing things OR Fred just left the party with Joe's wife." This is true either if the speaker is hallucinating or Fred is fooling around. It's even true if both of these things are true (though that seems unlikely). It's only false if both halves of the sentence are false.

The NOT gate (shown in Figure 5-3) is even simpler. It takes a single input and produces a single output — which is always the opposite of the input. Hence, if the input signal is a 0, the output signal will be a 1. And if the

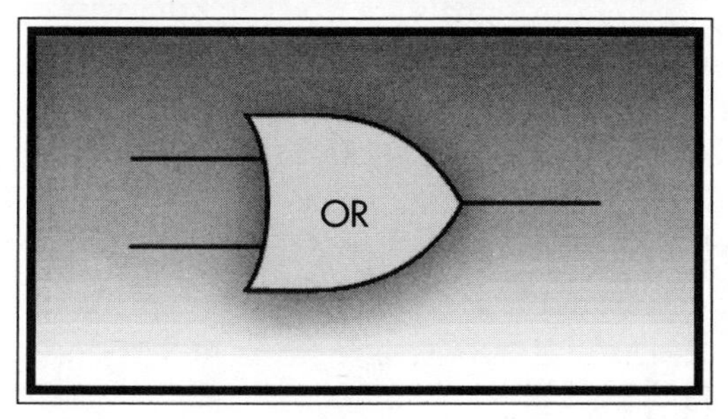

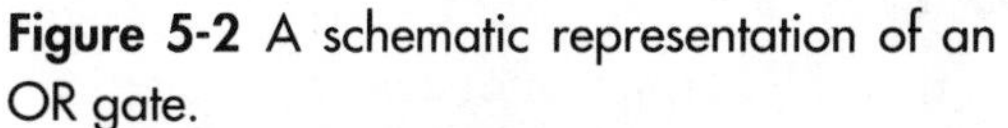

Figure 5-2 A schematic representation of an OR gate.

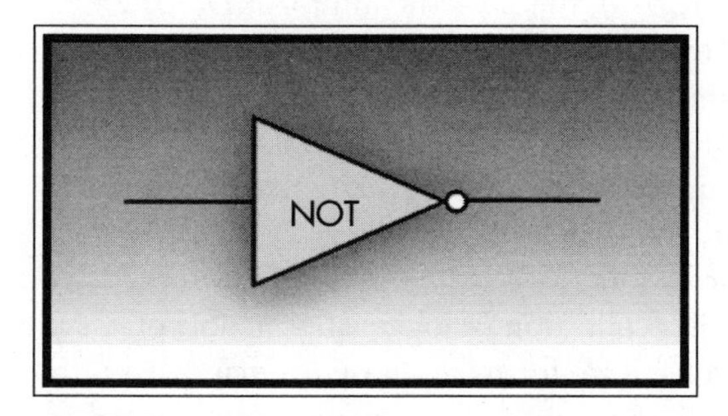

Figure 5-3 A schematic representation of a NOT gate.

input signal is a 1, the output signal will be 0. The NOT gate is equivalent to the English sentence, "I really enjoyed your piano recital last night, Jennifer . . . NOT!"

The AND, OR, and NOT gates can be combined to form other gates. One of the most common is the NAND gate, formed (as its name implies) from a NOT gate and an AND gate. (See Figure 5-4.) The output signal of the AND gate becomes the input signal of the NOT gate. Because the NOT gate reverses the output signal of the AND gate, the output signal of the NAND gate is precisely the opposite of that produced by the AND gate: it is false (0) only if the two input signals are true (1); otherwise, it is true. It is not, incidentally, necessary to combine an AND gate and a NOT gate to produce a NAND gate; the NAND gate can be constructed as a single circuit. Of course, that single circuit may contain an AND gate and a NOT gate on the inside, but computer designers never worry about what goes on *inside* a circuit. As long as the circuit is in good working order, they only care about what goes in and what comes out.

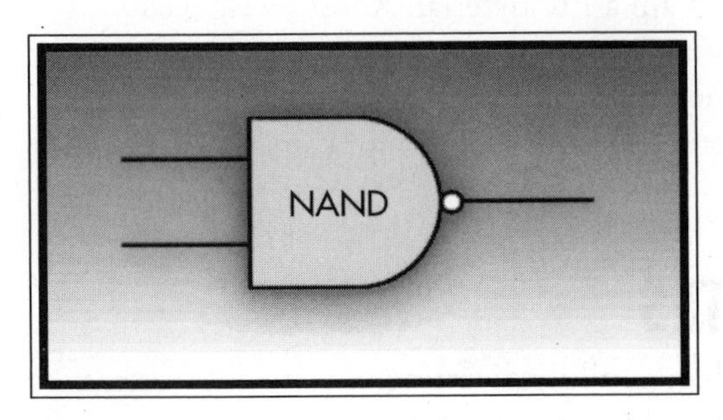

Figure 5-4 A schematic representation of a NAND gate.

THE CENTRAL PROCESSING UNIT

Once you start putting logic gates together, so that the outputs of one or more gates become the inputs to other gates (as in Figure 5-5), the sky's the limit. AND, OR, NOT, and NAND gates can be combined to perform any logical operations imaginable, arithmetic included. The right combination of gates can add two binary numbers, subtract two binary numbers from one another, or simply copy a number unchanged from the input circuitry to the output circuitry. Put enough logic circuits together and they can form the basis of a word processor, an electronic spreadsheet, or a video game.

In most computers, however, logic circuits are used primarily to construct *central processing units*, or CPUs for short. A CPU is a collection of logic gates capable of performing a wide variety of logical operations. Two forms of input are channeled into the CPU: programs and data. The program is a sequence of binary numbers that tells the CPU which of its wide array of logical operations it is to perform; the data are the

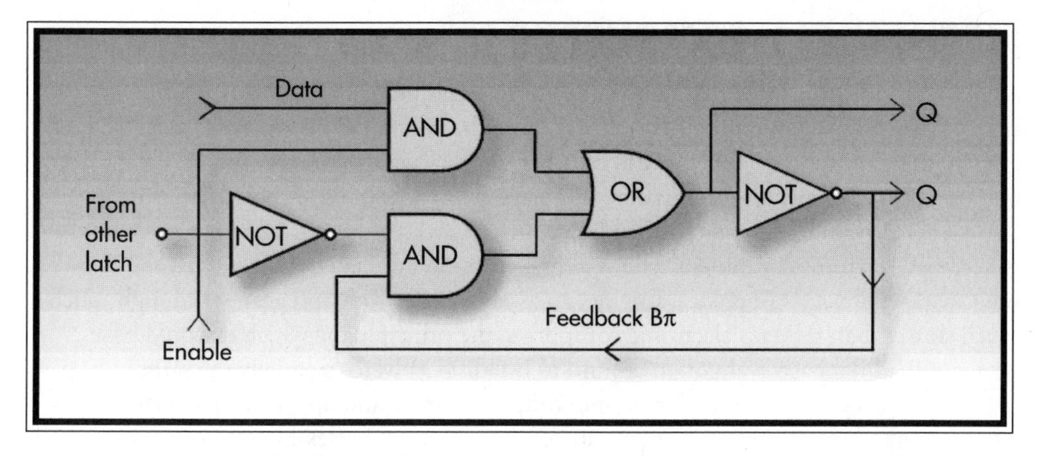

Figure 5-5 An example of several logic circuits combined so that the output of each gate becomes the input of another gate.

actual binary numbers that it is to perform those operations on. Since just about any kind of information — text, pictures, even music — can be represented as binary numbers, the CPU represents a kind of generic information processing unit that is "rewired" by the program to become the specific information process unit that the user of the computer currently needs. A properly constructed CPU can become any type of information processing device at all, given a programmer savvy enough to write the program. (Because programs change the behavior of the computer hardware so radically, they are often referred to as *software.*)

It seems amazing that such an incredibly useful and versatile device could be constructed out of nothing more than AND, OR, NOT, and NAND gates, yet it's true. In fact, it's possible to build a computer CPU out of nothing more than NAND gates.

To prove that nanocomputers are possible, at least in theory, it is only necessary to show that one can build a NAND gate on the molecular level, and that this nano-NAND gate can be linked to other NAND gates to form complex logic circuitry. And, in fact, Eric Drexler has designed not only NAND gates, but an entire host of logic devices that could potentially be built out of relatively small molecules. Whether these circuits can actually be built within the sorts of engineering restrictions we talked about in the last chapter has not yet been proven, but Drexler's analysis of the problem indicates that they can be.

MECHANICAL COMPUTERS

As we've already noted, the first nanocomputers we can model will almost certainly not be electronic in nature. To reflect this reality, Drexler has restricted his nanocomputer designs entirely to mechanical devices. Instead of using electric currents to carry binary signals from one circuit to the next, Drexler's nanocomputers use the motions of molecular rods.

There's nothing new about the idea of mechanical computers. In fact, it predates the concept of electronic computers. The very first computer designed (as far as anyone knows) was Charles Babbage's Analytical Engine, an assemblage of rods and gears. Although much, much slower than modern electronic computers, the principles by which it would have operated (had Babbage ever gotten around to building it) were essentially the same.

The rods of one of Drexler's nanocomputers are made up mostly of carbon atoms, bonded one after another in a sturdy but reasonably flexible sequence (in case the rod is called upon to snake its way around a corner). In a nanologic circuit, these rods will move in a piston-like manner through passageways between molecules. Protruding structures made from carbon, nitrogen, hydrogen, oxygen, silicon, and flourine atoms will be located at intervals along each rod. These structures come in two varieties, which Drexler calls gate knobs and probe knobs.

A MECHANICAL AND GATE

Look at rod A depicted in Figure 5-6. The two protrusions on rod A are probe knobs. This rod is crisscrossed by two other rods (B and C), in passageways perpendicular to the one containing rod A. At one end of rod A is a coiled spring. This spring is capable of pushing rod A forward down the passageway. However, it is prevented from doing so by the two squarish protrusions on rods B and C, which are blocking the probe knobs on rod A. These squarish protrusions are gate knobs, also called blocking knobs. (The shapes of these knobs are for symbolic purposes only and don't necessarily reflect the actual shape that such knobs will take in practice.)

If some force were to push rods B and C so that their gate knobs no longer blocked the probe knobs on rod A, rod A would move forward down the passageway under the pressure of the spring. Note, however, that both rods B and C would need to be moved out of the way at the same time. If only one of the two rods were moved, rod A would still be blocked by the other.

Does this sound familiar? Let's say, arbitrarily, that an unpushed rod represents a binary 0 and a pushed rod represents a binary 1. The contraption in Figure 5-6 magically becomes an AND gate, with rods B and C representing the input signals and rod

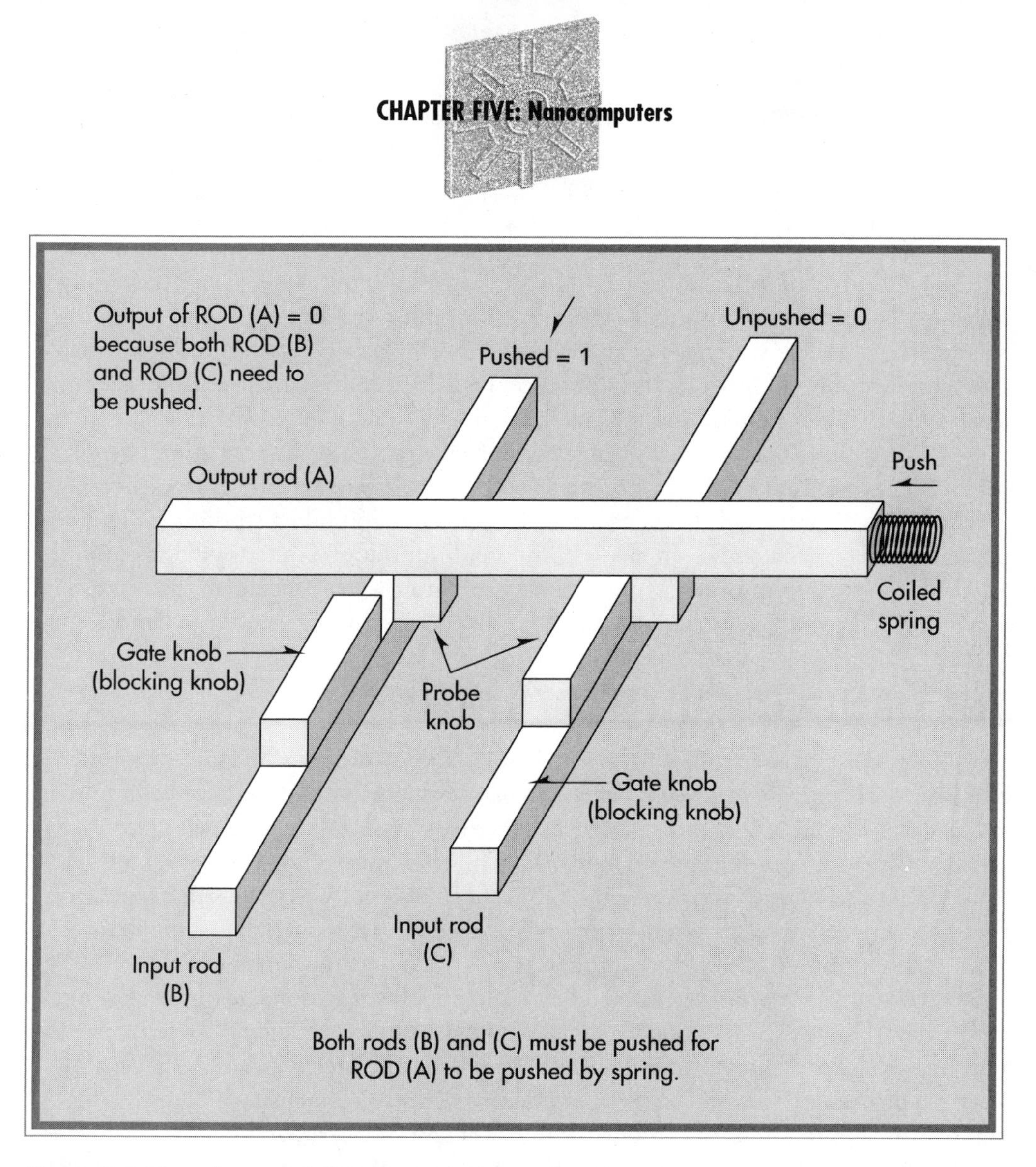

Figure 5-6 Three logic rods forming a mechanical AND gate.

A representing the output signal. A NAND gate could similarly be constructed by initially placing rods B and C so that they block rod A only *after* they have been pushed.

Where do our mechanical logic gates get their input signals (that is, the pressure that makes rods A and B move)? Probably from the output rods of other mechanical logic gates. And where does the output signal go? Most likely, it pushes an input rod on the next logic gate in the series.

OR gates and NOT gates could be constructed in a similar manner. However, once we have the ability to construct a NAND gate, we know that we have the ability to make a computer — in principle, at least. From this point on, everything else is an engineering problem, which is not to trivialize how difficult — or even insurmountable — such problems will prove to be in practice. Eric Drexler has suggested a number of techniques that may be used to build such circuits.

If you'd like to prove these principles yourself, you might want to stop by your neighborhood toy and hardware stores and pick up the necessary implements — a set of Tinkertoys™ and a tightly coiled spring. It's possible to build a working CPU out of these implements alone — in fact, a computer built out of Tinkertoys™ is currently on display in the Smithsonian Museum in Washington, D.C. — though the task isn't recommended to anyone who doesn't have a *lot* of spare time on his or her hands.

THE NANOCOMPUTER REVOLUTION

Obviously, these nanocircuits will be small, at least three orders of magnitude smaller than the most state-of-the-art integrated circuitry being produced today. These tiny circuits can be used in two different ways. The first is to build tiny nanocomputers to guide nanodevices around in the nanoworld. These computers could be programmed using molecular "tapes," not unlike the DNA molecules in living cells. Such tapes could be synthesized by nanoprogrammers using molecular sequencing equipment, then dissolved into the liquid environment where the nanocomputers work.

The second use would be to build extremely sophisticated macroscopic computer equipment. Not only will nanocircuitry allow huge numbers of logic gates to be packed into the same area as present-day computer chips, but the precise positioning capabilities of nanoassemblers will allow the development of three-dimensional computer chips, with circuits arranged through a volume of space rather than on a flat surface, as is currently the practice. This will roughly cube the number of circuits that can be put in a chip, in addition to the thousandfold gain in complexity due to the smaller circuit size. Nanocomputers will be sophisticated indeed.

This staggering increase in computer power will open up new application areas that simply aren't feasible with current computer designs, especially in calculation-intensive areas such as computer animation, simulation of real-world processes, and artificial intelligence. The power of a human brain could be replicated in nanocircuits that would take up only a fraction of the space occupied by a real brain. Drexler has suggested that smart machines able to solve engineering problems could be used to accelerate the design of future technol-

ogy, speeding up progress by a factor of many thousands.

Which means that most of the technological problems facing the human race might be solved within a few years of the nanocomputer revolution!

..."Perhaps I could interest you in some software?" the salesman said to the 12-year-old boy. "We just received a shipment of brand new hypervideo games. Would you like a copy of Nano-Invaders? War of the Super Brains? Secrets of the AI Masters?"

The boy gave the salesman a look of contempt. "I got all of those last month. Even my friends have played those. What do you have that's new?"

The salesman glanced around the showroom with a look of desperation on his face. "I'm afraid those are the latest ones we have. Er, would you be interested in buying an artificially intelligent companion with the latest in nanotechnological superbrains? Tells stories in 75 different languages. Performs advanced physics experiments. Never loses its temper."

"That's for babies," the boy said, obviously exasperated. "Look, I've gotta go. Maybe they've got some better stuff at Pete's Nanoware, across the street."

As soon as the boy had left the showroom, a man in a dark suit appeared from somewhere in the rear. He walked up behind the salesman and placed one hand gently between his shoulder blades. The salesman froze where he was standing, the expression on his face locking in place as though it had been cast in stone.

The man in the dark suit picked up the salesman and carried him toward the back of the store. "Some superbrain!" he muttered. "That's the last time I buy one of these nanorobot salespeople. This one couldn't even sell video games to a 12-year-old kid, for gosh sakes! How incompetent can you get?"

NANOMEDICINE: THE END OF DISEASE?

...There were times when the old man thought he'd be better off dead. He was nearly ninety years old and had been in ill health for many years. He spent his days in a wheelchair and his doctors gave him no hope of ever getting out of it. He was in constant pain. Drugs would have made the agony less insistent, but they would also dull his mind. And his mind was almost the only thing he had left.

Fortunately, he was rich. His wealth couldn't make him healthy, but at least it had made his twilight years easier to bear. At the moment he was being wheeled down a long corridor by one of his many servants. His presence had been requested by an old friend, a fellow octagenarian who had formerly been one of the most influential biochemists in the world. What in the world could the old fellow possibly want to see him about? They had pretty much stopped talking to each other over the years—it just seemed like there was nothing left to say. Surely now he must have something important to discuss.

The servant wheeled the old man through a narrow door and into a cluttered office. In the middle of the office was a wooden desk. Seated at the desk was a young man of about twenty-five.

"Where's Raymond?" the old man asked snappishly. He had long ago stopped engaging in formalities with people less than half his age. "He told me to be here at three o'clock. It's now 3:01. What happened? Did his wheelchair get stuck in traffic?"

The young man smiled. "I'm Raymond," he said.

"So you're his grandson, eh?" the old man said. "Raymond the third. Or is it fourth? Did the old boy send you to talk to me?"

"You could say that," the young man said. "There's been a tremendous scientific breakthrough and I wanted you to be one of the first to know about it. It hasn't been announced to the general public yet."

The old man's attention began wandering visibly. "I have no interest in scientific breakthroughs. Your grandfather could have told you that."

"I've been interested for quite a while in nanotechnology," the young man continued, unfazed by the old man's lack of interest. "I'm acquainted with some of the major researchers and often get early glimpses of their work. In this case, I got an early sample of it."

"Sample?" the old man said. "What are you talking about?"

The young man held up a small vial containing a clear liquid. "This is the world's first 100-percent- effective anti-aging drug. It reverses the aging process. Take one drink — and two days later all signs of aging and accompanying illness are gone."

"That's impossible!" the old man said, becoming visibly angry. "You're trying to sell me something, aren't you? What proof do you have of this outrageous claim?"

"Like I said," the young man told him, "I'm Raymond. I'll be 89 in November. Once, long ago, we were the best of friends. We

sat up all night in our college dormitory arguing about Kierkegaard and Sartre. We listened to music by Dave Brubeck and Dizzy Gillespie. We argued about life on other planets, and you always fell in love with the same women I did."

He held out the small vial. "I wanted to share this with you." After a long pause, the old man took it from him. After an even longer pause, he began to drink . . .

Most people have a love-hate relationship with the medical profession. As children, we are taught to see doctors as all-powerful healers, who will take away all of our ills. As adults, we sometimes shift to viewing doctors as money-hungry quacks, who make us feel worse as often as they make us feel better and take our money for the privilege.

The truth, as with most such things, is somewhere in between. Doctors are not all-powerful, but neither (for the most part) are they quacks. However, they are up against a significant obstacle. Doctors work on the macroscale. Diseases work on the nanoscale.

NANOSCALE EMERGENCIES

What happens when you become sick? That varies, obviously, depending on the disease, but it often starts on the molecular level. That's why most diseases have lengthy prodromal periods, during which the illness is at work in the body without the owner of the body necessarily being aware of it. Yet the molecular destruction, often within individual cells, has already begun. It just takes time for such nanoscale processes to start having macroscale effects: days, weeks, years. In a few cases, it can even take decades.

Many of the most common diseases — colds, flu, measles, chicken pox — are caused by viruses, which are formidable molecular machines in their own right. A virus consists of a shell of protein surrounding a tightly coiled strand of DNA. The protein shell is designed to attach itself to a living cell, usually a particular kind of cell. When it does so, it becomes a kind of miniature hypodermic needle, injecting the strand of DNA right through the cell wall. Once inside the cell, the DNA strands copy themselves into RNA and force the protein-synthesizing equipment of the cell to crank out new viruses. Eventually, the cell fills up with these viral copies and bursts, releasing the viruses into the intracellular environment, where they can find and infect new cells. (See Figure 6-1.)

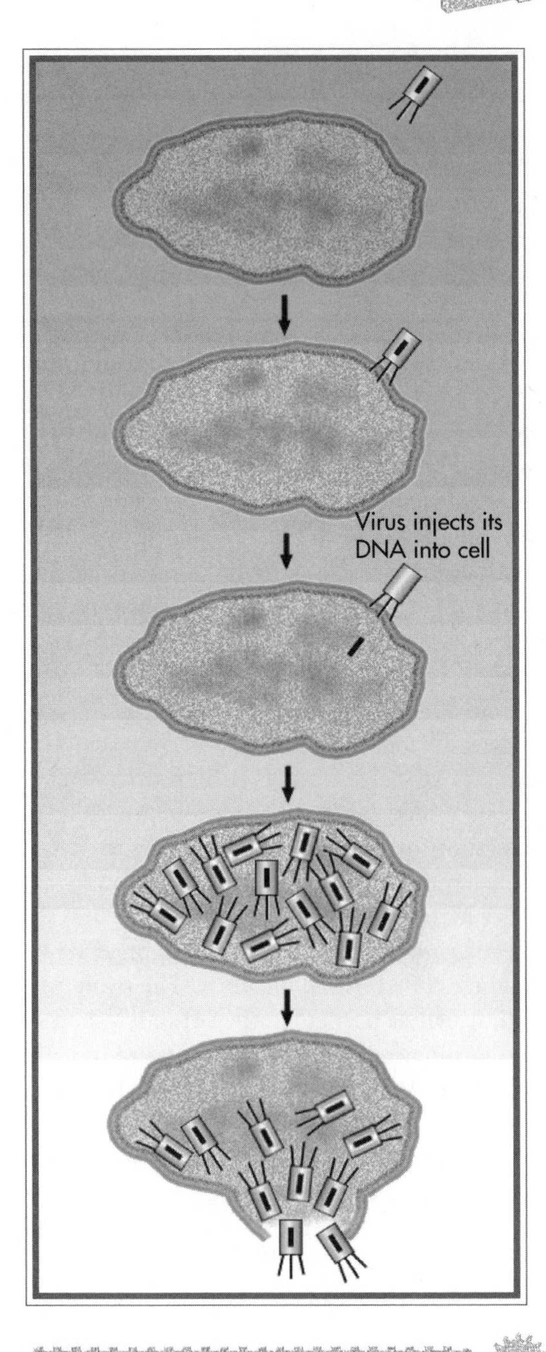

A rarer type of virus, the retrovirus, is far more insidious. Probably the best-known disease caused by a retrovirus is acquired immune defiency syndrome, better known as AIDS. The chief physical difference between a virus and a retrovirus is that the latter contains a coil of RNA rather than DNA inside its protein coat. But the modus operandi of the retrovirus is quite distinct: once inside a cell, the RNA copies itself into DNA (the reverse of the usual process by which DNA is copied into RNA, hence the "retro" in retrovirus) and uses tiny molecular scissors to insert itself into the cell's chromosomes. Then it does nothing. For months, perhaps years, the retrovirus genes can linger unnoticed in the heart of the cells, until a signal arrives telling the cell to begin manufacturing copies of the retrovirus. Where does this signal come from? What form does it take? No one is sure, but it is possible that other diseases may trigger the viral genes. This is how AIDS manages to reside nearly unnoticed in the body for long periods of time before manifesting itself in devastating ways.

Figure 6-1 One of the most sophisticated natural nanomachines at work. A virus injects its DNA into a cell; new viruses are created and then escape to infect other cells.

Some diseases are in the chromosomes all along; they are passed along from parent to child and usually only manifest themselves when they are contained in the chromosomes received from both parents. These hereditary diseases result from errors in the molecular sequences coding for the amino acids used to construct the body's natural nanomachinery. Because of these errors, some of these natural machines don't work correctly; in many instances, they don't work at all. The absence of critical machinery causes cellular processes to malfunction, which eventually leads to macroscale problems. Hereditary diseases include cystic fibrosis, sickle-cell anemia, Huntington's chorea, and Down's syndrome.

Not all diseases take place entirely on the nanoscale. Some operate closer to the microscale, the scale of the cells. Many diseases, for instance, are caused by living organisms, such as bacteria and other parasites, that invade the body and disrupt its operation. (Viruses are not precisely living organisms, though they have some things in common with living organisms.) Diseases caused by invading organisms include malaria, pneumonia, syphilis, tetanus, tuberculosis, dipththeria, and Rocky Mountain spotted fever. (See Figure 6-2.)

Heart disease is usually caused by the buildup of nanoscale particles in the circulatory system, which can form hard deposits known as plaque inside the arteries. When the arteries become sufficiently blocked, damage to the heart can occur, resulting in death or disability.

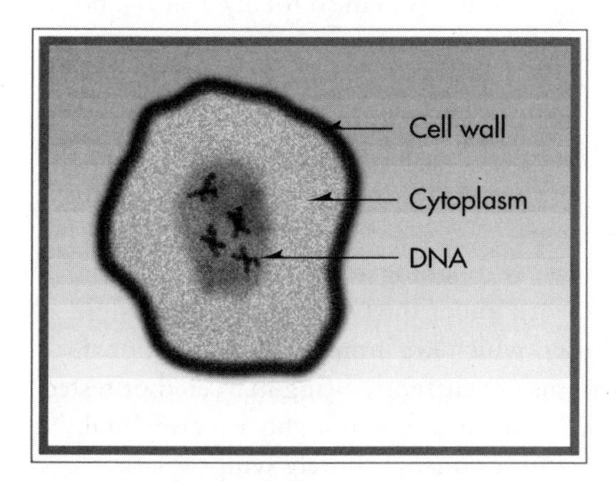

Figure 6-2 One of the most common disease-causing organisms: the bacterium.

Cancer is a disease that apparently begins on the nanoscale, through processes not yet completely understood, and slowly works its way to the microscale and then the macroscale. Something goes wrong in the genetic information of a cell, causing it to multiply wildly, producing deadly tumors that can spread throughout the body through a process known as metastasis, eventually wreaking havoc wherever they take root.

The body can become damaged in other ways than disease. Injury can traumatize large numbers of cells,

destroying tissue and disrupting the body's large-scale machinery — the circulatory system, the respiratory system, the nervous system — which is in turn constructed from molecular machinery. This damage can range from minor inconvenience (a cut finger) to medical emergency (a massive head wound).

THE IMMUNE SYSTEM

We are lucky in that our bodies have their own nanoscale and microscale mechanisms for fighting disease and repairing damaged subsystems. These mechanisms are so efficient and effective that we are generally not even aware that our bodies have been invaded by nanoscale and microscale intruders, so swiftly is the invasion repelled. Even cancer is usually dealt with in a summary manner by these defenses. Only when this immune system fails to rout the invaders before damage is done do we become ill, and even then the battle is usually won by the body in the end.

Alas, the immune system can't win every battle. Sometimes, when the body is weakened by other diseases, or by general mistreatment, it will eventually succumb to illnesses that the immune system can usually defeat, such as the flu. And a small minority of diseases have the frightening ability to bypass the immune system completely. Herpes is one; this virus takes up residence in the nervous system and emerges at intervals to create an irritating and contagious rash. AIDS is another. Far more devastating than herpes, AIDS can cripple the immune system so totally that the body eventually succumbs to diseases it could normally resist with ease.

When the body is injured, it puts its natural healing processes to work repairing damaged tissue. The body's nanomachinery begins stimulating the growth of new cells to replace those that have been lost. If the injury is especially severe, the body shuts down much of its nonessential activity and reroutes its resources to the injured tissue until the most critical damage has been repaired.

Much of modern medicine concerns itself with aiding and abetting the natural machinery of the body, allowing it to do its work under the best conditions possible. This is the *only* effective way of treating viruses, which are immune to conventional medication. (A number of antiviral medications are currently being marketed or tested by drug companies, but most are only partially effective or still highly experimental. No surefire cures have been developed.) Treatment for viruses is purely symptomatic, helping the patient feel better until the invaders have been repelled by the body.

Nonetheless, modern medicine has made tremendous strides in treating a number of once devastating illnesses. After decades of experimentation, doctors and biologists have found a number of ways to intervene in the disease process. This intervention can take two forms, often used in conjunction with one another: surgery and drugs. In many cases, however, this intervention can be almost as threatening to the patient as the disease it is intended to cure.

SURGERY AND DRUGS

The first, surgery, is a bulk technology, albeit one that is somewhat more precise than a bulldozer scooping rocks off of a highway. On the nanoscale, though, a surgeon's knife is as destructive as a thousand bulldozers, destroying cells by the millions, disrupting the nanoscale machinery of the body in uncountable ways. No patient *wants* to undergo major surgery, unless it is the only alternative to something even worse, like death or constant pain. In the most extreme cases, the surgery is only marginally less likely to kill the patient than the disease itself. But when the alternative is certain death, even a 10 percent survival rate begins to look pretty good. Thankfully, the survival rate for most types of surgery is a lot better than that.

Drugs, by contrast, are a molecular technology, if a somewhat haphazard one. A pill or a spoonful of medicine contains millions of tiny molecules, many of which would qualify as simple nanodevices, which enter the body and correct molecular deficiencies or intervene in processes that have somehow gone awry. (See Figure 6-3.) Many of these molecules have been "borrowed" from nature. Antibiotics, for instance, are produced naturally by certain species of bacteria as a way of fighting off competing species of bacteria. Many plants produce molecules useful in fighting disease and alleviating pain. Drugs can also be produced in the laboratory, through natural chemical processes.

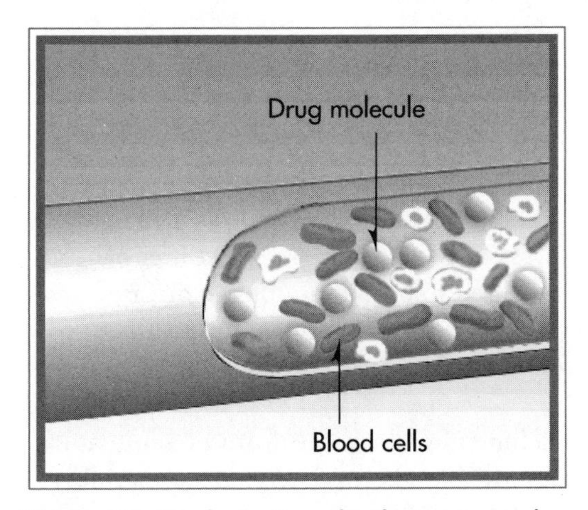

Figure 6-3 On the nanoscale, drugs are crude molecular devices that interact with the molecular machinery of your body.

Because they work on the nanoscale — the scale on which the

diseases themselves tend to operate — drugs are usually a safer and more efficient means of fighting disease than surgery and are therefore always the treatment of first resort. But drugs also have their drawbacks. In many cases, there is simply no drug available to perform the job that needs to be done. Viruses, as we have noted, are largely immune to drug therapy.

Worse, most drugs have unintended side effects. This is almost inevitable with drugs found in nature, since we are using these drugs for purposes they were not necessarily intended to fulfill. For instance, a medicine used to fight convulsions might be created from a chemical used by a fish to paralyze its enemies. Or a drug that dulls pain may have originally been secreted by a plant to drug animals into unconscious submission. No wonder these drugs have effects they were not supposed to have. (That's why a typical bottle of narcotic pain relievers has a warning on the side telling you not to operate heavy machinery while using it because it may cause drowsiness. Why should a pain reliever make you drowsy? No reason, but this is a typical side effect.)

Drugs manufactured by chemical processes present a somewhat different problem. While in theory these drugs could be tailored to have precisely the effect that is intended, in practice we don't yet understand enough about how these drugs work to approximate the desired effect more than very closely. In some cases, we have *no* idea why the drugs work, just that they do. And thus it is difficult to determine how to get rid of any unwanted side effects that may crop up.

NANODRUGS

The ideal way to design drugs would be to start with a perfect model of the disease process itself, then design a molecular machine that would stop that process in its tracks and put the body back into the shape it was in before the disease struck. Enter nanotechnology. In theory, nanomedicines could be used to both examine the disease process, tracking the course of microorganisms and tissue damage, and to stop that process and put the body back together again. All without the patient necessarily being aware that he or she is even sick.

An all-purpose disease-fighting nanomachine might take the form of a miniature submarine that would navigate its way through the bloodstream. In that submarine would be a powerful nanocomputer. (Eric Drexler estimates that such a submarine could carry a computer as powerful as the large mainframes of the mid-1980s.) This computer would be programmed to seek out and destroy disease-causing organisms. Sensor devices attached to the submarine would examine all objects it encountered,

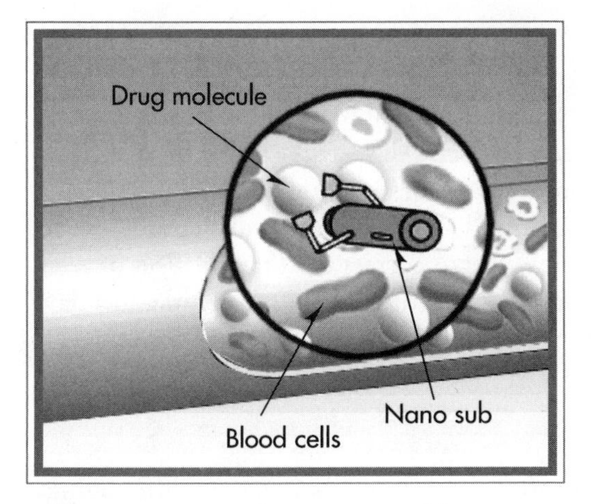

Figure 6-4 Nanosubmarines could navigate through the bloodstream, searching for invading organisms.

studying their shapes and surface molecules, and comparing them with a database of known disease organisms stored in the computer's memory banks. When a pathogen is encountered, it could be destroyed, broken down into its molecular building blocks. (See Figure 6-4.)

How does this differ from what the immune system already does? In many instances, the immune system can only mount a full-fledged defense against organisms that the body has already encountered and can recognize. But the nanosubmarine's computer could recognize any organism known to medical science — a list that will grow quickly as such nanomachines explore the bodily environment and send back reports of what they find there.

Nanodevices could be designed for specific health care needs — chipping away at plaque-blocking arteries, cleaning tooth enamel and skin pores, dissolving cancerous tumors. Eric Drexler envisions nanomachines that would "herd cells," moving cells into areas of injured tissue and forcing them to multiply rapidly so as to replace cells that have been lost or damaged in an accident.

These carefully engineered nanoscale processes would (in theory, at least) have no unwanted side effects, since they are tailored precisely for the tasks that they are intended to perform, in full knowledge of the environment in which they will perform them. And when full knowledge of that environment isn't available, the computer programs on board the devices will utilize complex algorithms to decide what approach to the problem is most likely to solve it, an option not available to the mindless machinery of the immune system.

It should be noted here, of course, that early nanomachines — medical and otherwise — will be far from perfect. The first experimental nanocures will probably have unexpected side effects, perhaps far worse than the medicines that they are replacing — which certainly calls for cautious testing. But these side effects can be quickly removed, because of the greater control that nanotechnology affords us over the structure of manmade nanomachines. With luck, most of the unexpected side effects will be dealt with in early experiments, perhaps even in computer models of the process.

Genetic diseases, virtually untouched by conventional medicine, will be easily cured through nanomedicine. Once the specific genetic flaws that caused these diseases are understood — and many of them are on the verge of being understood today — it will be a simple task for a nanosubmarine to extend a chromosome-editing tool into a cell and edit the sequence of molecules in the genes to correct the error. A fleet of billions or trillions of nanomachines could repair all of the cells in a body in a few days or even hours.

THE END OF AGING?

One of the most incredible possibilities suggested for nanomedicine is to "cure" aging. This might seem paradoxical at first blush. How can something as normal as aging be cured? It isn't even a disease.

Yet, in a sense, aging is a disease. It represents the slow degeneration of the body's molecular machinery. At some point, that machinery ceases to be capable of fighting off the effects of disease and injury and the body stops functioning. We die of old age. In this light, age can be looked at as a degenerative disease from which we all inevitably suffer.

If aging is a disease, then nanomedicine can fight it. It is possible, in fact, that aging is simply the slow accumulation of errors in the chromosomes at the hearts of the cells. If so, it might be relatively easy to design a nanosubmarine that could proofread the chromosomes and repair these errors before they accumulate to a fatal level. Such a nanosub could have six proofreading devices attached to it on long molecular cables. Each device would enter a different cell and read the chromosomes. The central nanocomputer would compare the chromosomes, looking for differences in the molecular sequences. When a cell is found to contain a different chromosomal sequence than any of its neighbors, that sequence can be corrected. (See Figure 6-5.)

After these repairs are complete, the body would slowly revert to its optimum state, equivalent to an individual in his or her mid-twenties. The "aging treatment" would probably take the form of swallowing a glass full of liquid in which billions of nanomachines lurked unseen, waiting to begin the repair work. Individuals could choose to take this treatment as often or as rarely as they wish. Certainly, anyone who actually wishes to grow old should be allowed to do so.

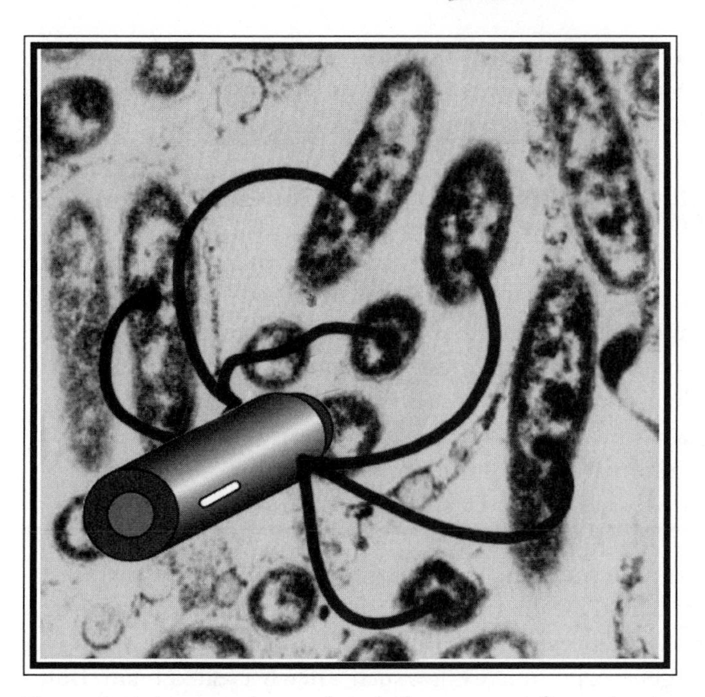

Figure 6-5 A nanosub proofreads the genetic information in six cells simultaneously.

DIAGNOSING DISEASE

An area where nanotechnology will prove particularly useful is in the diagnosis of disease. Currently, most diagnosis *is* done on a symptomatic basis. The patient describes the symptoms of the disease to a doctor, who draws on his or her vast knowledge of human ailments (with a little help from books and computer databases) to determine just what the patient is suffering from. Although it might seem easy enough to identify the nature of a disease from a description of symptoms, it really isn't. Many diseases have pretty much the same symptoms. (In fact, many of these symptoms result from the action of the body's disease-fighting mechanisms, not from the disease itself.) And the descriptions given by patients are often less than clear.

To further determine the nature of a disease, it is often necessary to examine a patient's body in some detail. This can be done through such noninvasive procedures as X-rays or magnetic resonance imaging or through chemical assays of fluids (usually blood or urine) taken from the body. As a last resort, a surgeon can actually cut open the body and look inside, a process known as exploratory surgery.

Obviously, exploratory surgery has its drawbacks. But the other processes have drawbacks as well. X-rays can actually damage the molecular structure of the body and frequently fail to detect the very problems that they are searching for. Chemical assays work quite well for some diseases, poorly for others.

Nanomachines, however, could search the body for problems on a molecular level. With trillions of machines at work, there is virtually no problem that could not be found in a few hours at the nanolevel, and with no side effects to speak of.

THE LIMITS OF NANOMEDICINE

Is there anything that nanomedicine won't be able to fix? The truth is, not much will lie beyond nanotechnology's grasp, at least potentially. There is, however, one situation that might stretch it to the limit and a little beyond — injuries to the brain. Over a lifetime, the human brain becomes etched with a vast amount of knowledge, held in place by a vast number of cellular interconnections. If the brain is damaged, or if something interrupts the flow of nutrients to the brain, this information can be lost, partially or *in toto.* And once information is lost, it cannot be regained, at least not precisely. (Any computer user who has suffered a hard-disk crash when no backup is available understands what a difficult truth this is.)

Even nanotechnology cannot restore the lost contents of the mind. At best, nanomachines can reconstruct blank, informationless brain cells, giving the lost parts of the brain the ability to function at the level of a newborn child. Perhaps someday it will even be possible to impress a "generic personality" on such a newly created brain. But unless we can find some way to record the contents of a person's brain and restore the information in that recording after brain damage has occurred, the original personality and knowledge of the brain can never be put back into place. In a real way, the brain's owner will be dead.

...The view from the summit was spectacular. It had been a long climb, but it was worth it. He felt better than he'd felt in years. Hell, he felt better than he'd ever felt!

"You're pretty spry, for a 90-year-old," Raymond said, pulling a sandwich out of his backpack and handing it to him. "Here, take this. You need it more than I do. After all, you're nine weeks older than I am."

"Eight weeks and six days," he pointed out, taking the sandwich. "You never would give me the benefit of that extra day."

He stretched out on one elbow and nibbled at the sandwich, as he watched the sun slowly sink below the horizon. How many years had it been since he'd watched the sun set? He hadn't realized how much he'd missed it.

"We'd better get back down the mountain," Raymond said, as the last sliver of molten sunlight disappeared from sight. "It's an easy hike, but I'd like to finish the first part before total darkness sets in. We're having dinner at that little inn down in the village, remember?"

"That's right," he said, rising to his feet and brushing the dust from his clothing. "You said you were going to introduce me to that young waitress you've been dating."

"Only if you promise not to fall in love with her," Raymond said.

"I'll promise," he said. "But I'll be lying."

On the way back down, he was careful to keep his distance from the sharp precipice that ran partway along the edge of the summit. It was a long way down and even nanomachines could only repair so much damage.

After all, he was much too young to die.

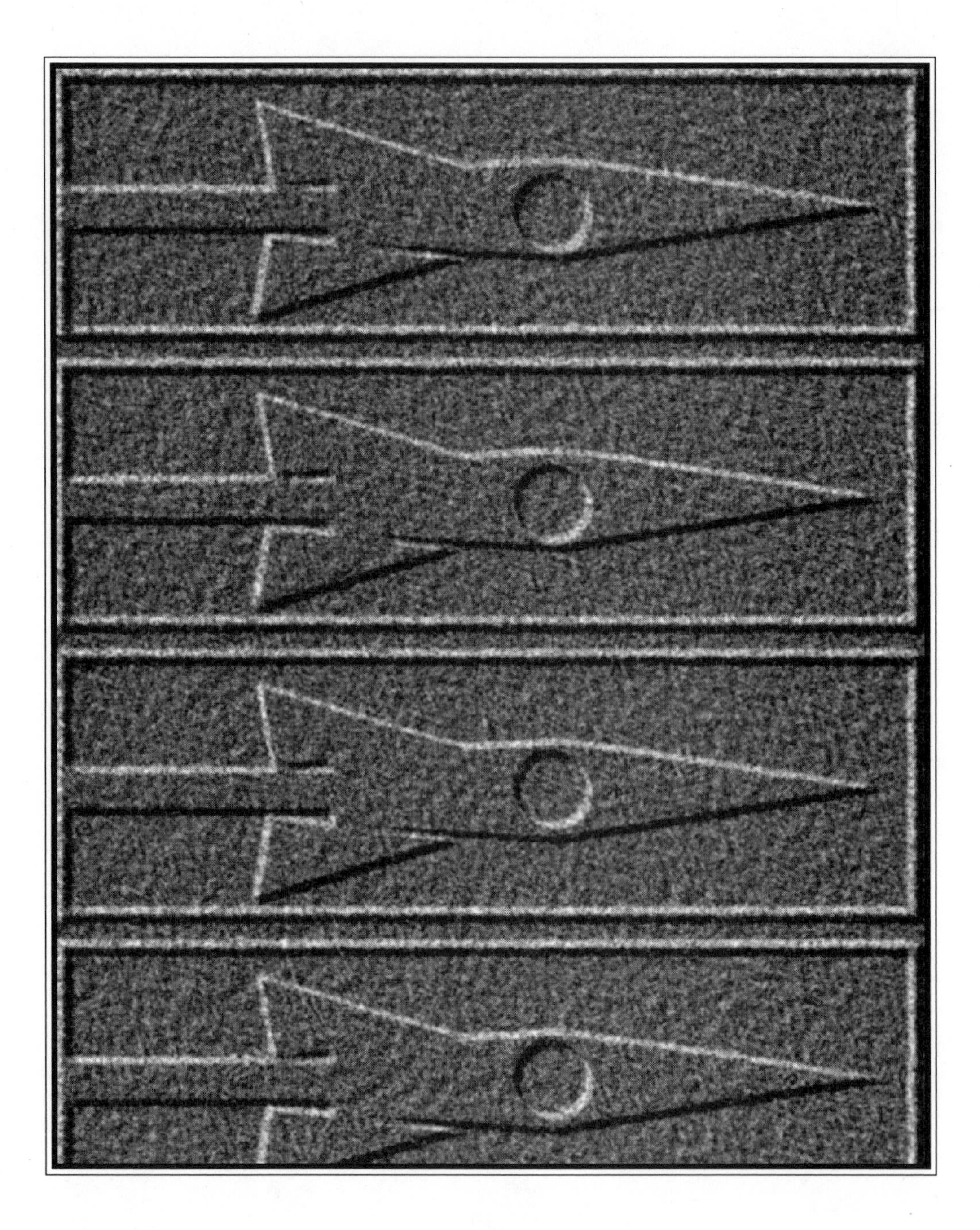

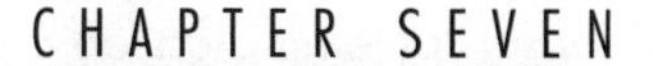

NANOMANUFACTURING: FROM THE SMALL SCALE TO THE LARGE

It wasn't like he couldn't get better roles, the actor thought. He had gotten rave reviews as Falstaff in Henry IV *and as Sancho Panza in* Man of La Mancha. *But there just weren't that many parts for men his size. He was, to be charitable about it, a large man. No, he was more than that: he was huge. The earth shook when he walked. He had been known to get stuck while going through doors.*

So when a small start-up company called General Nanotech had put out a call for large actors, he had been the first in line. And they had hired him on the spot.

But now he was having second thoughts about straying so far from the legitimate stage. It had sounded like a great deal at first.

The company had developed something called a portable molecular manufacturer, and he was supposed to demonstrate it as part of a stunt intended to garner publicity for the company. All he had to do was push a few buttons, speak a few lines of dialogue, and pick up his paycheck.

Except that the place where he was supposed to demonstrate it was the poorest section of the city. And the night he was supposed to demonstrate it on had turned out to be the coldest of the year. Now, as he stood in the middle of a deserted street next to the portable whatchamacallit, it was actually beginning to snow. The costume that the company had given him to wear was warm — but it wasn't that warm!

He was seriously considering catching a cab, heading back to his apartment, and phoning in his resignation. Alas, cabs didn't come to that part of town. The drivers were afraid of being mugged.

The actor began to wonder if the cab drivers might not have a point; dark figures were moving in the shadows at the edge of the street. He was wondering if he shouldn't have brought a weapon or some kind for protection. And then one of the shadowy figures stepped into the middle of the street. It was a child!

The child couldn't have been more than seven years old. She had dark skin and wide eyes, which grew even wider as she approached the spot where the actor was standing.

"Are you really?..." she asked tentatively.

"Yes, I am," he said. "Absolutely. Positively. You bet."

"I'm glad to meet you," the child said.

"I'm, uh, glad to meet you too," the actor told her.

As if emboldened by the first child's foray into the street, other children began to appear from the shadows. There were black children, white children, Latino children, Asian children. The only thing that they had in common, the actor noticed, was the enraptured way in which they looked up at him.

The demonstration! He had almost forgotten. That's what he was here for. He might as well get it over with.

The actor pushed a few buttons on the side of the molecular manufacturer. There was a whirring noise from within and after a few moments a door opened in the side of the machine.

Out poured toys, hundreds of them. There were large toys and small toys, toys for young children and toys for adolescents. There were dolls,

miniature airplanes, plush animals, ray guns, coloring books, tricycles, toys with flashing lights, toys that made loud noises. There were more toys than the actor had ever seen outside of a toy store, and they were all flowing from somewhere inside the molecular manufacturer. Where in the world were they all coming from?

The children knew what to do with them. They descended upon the toys with a great cry of delight. There was no fighting over the toys; there were quite enough to go around.

And then the actor remembered his dialogue. How unprofessional of him to forget! When he tried to speak, though, he noticed that there was a catch in his throat. And could that be a tear running down his cheek?

"Ho, ho, ho!" he exclaimed loudly. "Merry Christmas, everybody!"

He was surprised to discover that his laughter was quite genuine. He wasn't acting at all. And when he looked down at his ample stomach, hidden beneath the red costume that the company had given him, he realized that what he had heard was true.

It really did shake like a bowl full of jelly when he laughed!...

By their very nature, nanomachines will work on a very small scale. For the most part, this is a good thing. We *want* nanomachines to work on a small scale. That's their whole reason for existing.

Yet this small scale would also seem to be something of a disadvantage. Earlier, we talked about using nanomachines to manufacture macroscale objects: metal beams, automobile engines, electronic devices. But how can something as small as a nano-assembler turn out something as large as an eight-cylinder engine? Or an I-beam?

At first blush, this would seem a nearly insurmountable problem. Working an atom at a time, a minuscule nanofactory can crank out other molecular machines almost as quickly as the ribosomes in our cells turn out proteins, which is fast indeed. But this same atom-by-atom approach would take days, weeks, perhaps even years to create a macroscale object. How do we get around this dilemma?

SELF-REPLICATION

The solution is a process known as self-replication, first suggested decades ago for use in the space program (and discovered by the natural nanomachines in our bodies long before that). A self-replicator is a machine that can make copies of itself. (Human beings perform a kind of self-replication, though the process requires a *pair* of "machines" and never produces an exact replica.) Nanoassemblers, which can build anything, can be programmed to crank out other nanoassemblers; thus they qualify as self-replicators. Special procedures will be needed to create copies of the program used by the assembler to assemble copies of itself, but that won't be a major problem.

Once you have a self-replicating machine, along with sufficient supplies of fuel and raw materials to keep it going, you can have as many copies of the machine as you want, simply by putting it to work making copies of itself. Although you might think it would take a long time to turn out, say, one trillion nanoassemblers, it actually doesn't. The trick is to have the copies of the first machine *also* make copies of themselves, and the copies of the copies make still more copies, and so forth. Anyone familiar with the powers of the number two knows what happens next. If a machine takes half an hour to copy itself (which may be a pessimistic estimate), then after half an hour there will be 2 machines. But after an hour there will be 4, after 2 hours (or 4 half hours) there will be 16, after four hours there will be 256, and so on. At this rate, it would only take about 15 hours to make a trillion machines, given enough raw materials. (Since the size of the machines is quite small, the amount of raw materials required to build a trillion machines is probably not prohibitively large.) (See Figure 7-1.)

Many nanomachines make light work. Once you have a trillion machines (or even a reasonably large fraction of a trillion machines), building macroscale structures is a piece of cake. Just put them all to work at once, each performing a tiny piece of the job. Before you know it, the job will be done.

Thus, most nanomanufacturing jobs will consist of two steps: replicating a large enough number of machines to do the job, followed by the actual construction. (There may also be a brief intermediate step, where the self-replicating assemblers turn out copies of special-purpose nanomanufacturing devices that have been optimized for the particular task at hand.) The first step will probably be the most time consuming. Once a large number of machines is in place, the actual manufacturing will probably proceed quite quickly.

QUALITY VS. QUANTITY

It should be clear by now that nanomachines can *make* just about anything. But what *should* we use them to make? What is the appropriate use of nanotechnology in manufacturing? It is tempting to reply that we should use it to make just about anything. And, in fact, this may be the appropriate answer.

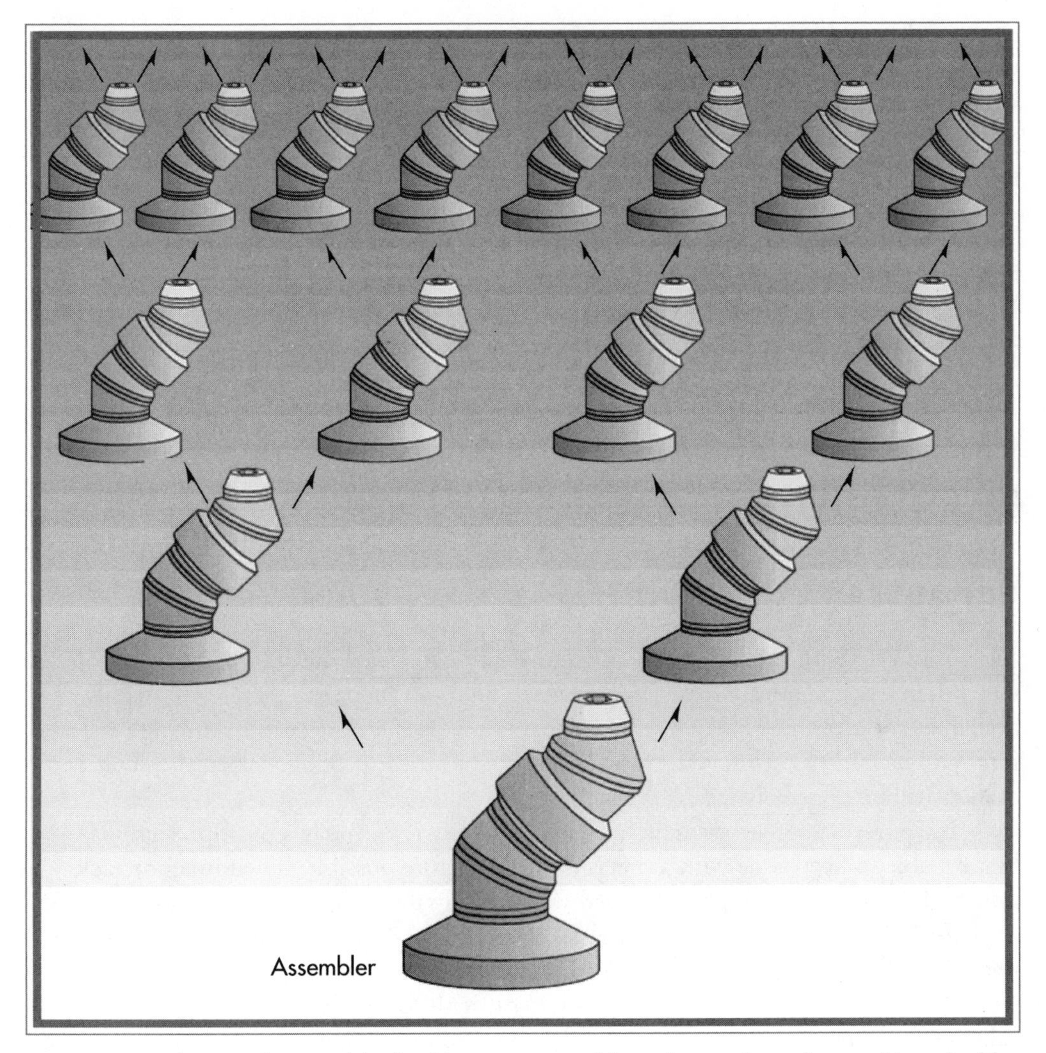

Figure 7-1 When each assembler builds more assemblers, the number of assemblers doubles with each generation.

In the modern world, we are used to regarding manufacturing processes as a series of trade-offs. We can make things cheaply, we can make things quickly, and we can make them well. But we can almost never do all three of these things at the same time. Thus, we must decide which one or two of these things is most important to us: economy, speed, or quality. Do we want to spend as little money as possible? Do we want it as quickly as possible? Or do we want it done *right* ?

It is almost axiomatic that quantity (which implies economy and speed) is antithetical to quality. But in the nanotechnological world, that may no longer be true. Because they build things with atomic-scale precision, nanomachines will turn out products of a higher quality than has ever been seen before. Yet they will also work cheaply and at lightning speed. Thus the distinction between quantity and quality may rapidly disappear. (To some extent, this has already begun happening in the various subfields of digital electronics, where the difference between high-end and low-end products have narrowed considerably in recent years, partly as the result of precision microscale manufacturing.)

ECONOMY

Just about anything that can be manufactured by nanomachines can be built out of fewer than a dozen different types of atoms, which can be put together into readily available and extremely inexpensive raw materials. Because the manufacturing process itself will be largely automated, the eventual cost of these products when they come to market will be extremely low.

Imagine analog wristwatches, higher in quality than today's most prestigious brands, able to keep time with a precision never before possible. Then imagine rack after rack of these stunningly fashioned watches on sale in the neighborhood discount mart for $10 apiece. Anyone will be able to afford a high-quality timepiece. Of course, once anyone can afford them, wearing a high-quality wristwatch will immediately lose its snob value. In fact, it will be increasingly difficult for *anything* to maintain its snob value in the nanoworld, which may not be a bad thing. Perhaps the snobs of the world will be forced to renounce all of their nanotechnologically manufactured goods and settle down to a life of organic farming in an effort to find a lifestyle that isn't affordable by the riff-raff.

Wristwatches won't be the only thing that will be cheap in the nanoworld. Imagine automobiles that sell for a few hundred dollars — or less — yet have more engine power, get greater fuel efficiency, and provide better passenger comfort than any on the market today. Or a desktop computer for $50 that is as fast and powerful as a supercomputer of the 1990s.

HARDWARE AS SOFTWARE

What will make nanogoods so cheap is that they will be as much software as they are hardware. Because nanomanufacturing will use standard assembling devices and raw materials, the only difference between one manufacturing task and the next will be the program tapes that tell the assemblers what to build. These program tapes, the software for the nanocomputers that guide the assemblers through their paces, will contain precise molecular specifications for whatever is to be built, be it wristwatch, automobile, or computer. Thus, before the nanofactories can make a product, a program must be written for that product.

It would seem like a daunting task to write a program for a wristwatch, or a computer, or an automobile. And it will be — at first. But just as most computers today are manufactured from standard parts, so the *program* for a computer will be put together from standard software modules, an approach already used in the creation of sophisticated computer software. Once someone has written a successful program for, say, a disk drive, he or she can sell this program to programmers writing programs for complete computers. The program for the disk drive could then be incorporated as a subprogram (or *function*, as it would be called in some current programming languages) in the larger program for the computer.

The program for an automobile might look something like this:

```
PROGRAM Rolls_Royce;

MAIN
  Wheels(4,rubber,chrome_hubcaps);
  Frame(standard_chassis,grey);
  Dashboard(walnut);
  Upholstery(black,leather);
  Hood_Ornament(chrome_R);
  Accessories(car_phone,stereo,CD_player);
END_MAIN;
```

and so forth, where each lowercase line of the program represents a "call" to a subprogram, possibly written by a different programmer, that generates that specific part of the finished product. Thus, such programs will become easier and easier to write as libraries of subprograms are assembled to perform unusually complex tasks. Of course, a *real* program for an automobile would also need to specify the three-dimensional relationship between the parts, the manner in which they would be physically attached to one another, and so forth. But we'll let a future generation of nanoprogrammers work out those details.

In effect, nanotechnology makes *everything* into software. We'll be able to build, swiftly and efficiently, anything that we can write a program for. And, over time, these programs will become more and more complex. Eventually, it will be possible to write programs for manufacturing things that quite simply cannot be manufactured today, at least through artificial processes, such as food. It may even be possible to manufacture living organisms, such as plants. After all, living things are merely extremely complicated assemblies of atoms. As such, they can be put together by nanomachines, at least in theory.

Of course, anybody who has been in a software store recently knows that software isn't precisely cheap. A product that consists of a cardboard box, a few manuals, and a stack of floppy disks — components that couldn't have a manufacturing cost of more than $10 — may sell for hundreds, even thousands, of dollars. What makes software so expensive is not manufacturing costs, but the expense of paying the salaries of a large programming team over the months and years required to create a truly sophisticated computer program. Because the sales of a special-purpose piece of software may not be all that large, the cost per copy must be increased to take up the slack.

Early nanoprograms may be quite expensive to produce too, and so the first nanoproducts won't be particularly cheap. But as these programs are used over and over again, economies of scale will come into play. Because the per-item cost of nanomanufacture is small, the cost of the nanoprogram can be deferred over large numbers of units, at least on popular items. Only esoteric items required by a few people (and made up of component parts that are themselves fairly unusual) will be expensive to make. And, in fact, it might be better to do so using old-fashioned methods, rather than writing nanoprograms on an ad hoc basis.

SPEED

Even though it is done a few atoms at a time, nanomanufacturing will be extremely fast, because of the large number of nanomachines that can be at work at one time. Only the initial stage, during which the nanomachines undergo self-replication, will be at all time consuming, and even that will probably be more rapid than we assumed in our earlier example. And once that is out of the way, one item after another can be rapidly turned out of the nanofactory.

QUALITY

Why will objects manufactured nanotechnologically be of higher quality than objects manufactured through conventional processes? There are a number of reasons.

One has to do with materials. Today, manufacturing is performed using materials that either occur in nature or that can be formed using conventional bulk chemical processes. But nanotech manufacturing will allow materials to be put together a few atoms at a time, with any internal structure allowed by the laws of physics and chemistry. Instead of relying on materials that are good enough, we will be able to build with materials that are nearly perfect for the task at hand.

Another has to do with flaws. Because the bulk manufacturing technologies of today are not capable of precise positioning of atoms, those atoms sometimes end up where they are not supposed to be. This is pretty much unavoidable, and the best we can hope for is that they end up someplace where they won't cause much trouble. But every now and then a serious flaw results in a manufactured object. These flaws can have tragic results — if they are part of the structure of a bridge, for instance. We have come to accept this as an inevitable fact of life: manufactured objects sometimes fail, often cataclysmically.

Objects manufactured nanotechnologically may not be without flaw, but any flaws that slip through will be on the level of individual atoms and molecules and probably won't have any macroscale effects. The sort of gross flaws currently found in macroscopically manufactured materials may cease to exist.

Of course, some objects are conceptually flawed — that is, the design itself is bad. This will be as true of nanotechnologically manufactured objects as of the present-day kind. This may always be a fact of life. Bad designs are eventually weeded out by a kind of Darwinian selection process, but not always before they cause trouble.

MOLECULAR MANUFACTURING AT WORK

With all of the above in mind, let's look at what might be a typical manufacturing process of the year 2050. Before us sits a large ceramic vat, with multiple tubes running into and out of it. At the flip of a switch, a fluid containing the raw material for building nanoassemblers is pumped into the vat through one of the tubes. Through another, much narrower tube, are introduced the "nanoseeds" — the initial few assemblers that are to make copies of themselves. The copying process will take about seven hours, so we start this process running first thing in the morning, then come back to check its progress in mid-afternoon.

By this time, the initial copying is complete. As we return to the vat, we hear a new chemical rushing through the tube. This chemical, triggered by the computer next to the vat, is a molecular "signal" that tells the assemblers to begin the next phase of the process. More raw materials are pumped into the vat, along with tiny programming tapes that enter the vat through one of the narrowest tubes. Inside, trillions of assemblers set to work on their final manufacturing task. After about an hour, it is complete. The vat is flushed clean of assemblers and raw materials. Once it has been emptied, a door on the side of the vat is opened. Inside is a shiny new automobile, the body seamlessly constructed around the engine and the interior. All parts are in place. There's even fuel in the tank. You enter the vat, climb into the automobile and drive it away. Total price of parts — $100. Total cost of labor — $0. The most expensive part was the program that told the assemblers how to perform the final part of the job. And that was on sale at Joe's Bargain Nanosofts, where you shop regularly.

Where was all of this happening? In the garage in the back of your house. You use the big machine every day, cranking out everything you happen to own software for building. When you end up with a manufacturing surplus, you trade the oversupply with your neighbors, who have software for building things you cannot.

The truth is, you hardly ever shop anyplace but Joe's any more.

...Most of the children were gone. The molecular manufacturer had produced its last toy and now sat silently in the street. Great fluffy snowflakes dropped out of the sky and lodged themselves in the actor's phony beard.

It was time to go. The photographers from the local paper had shown up right on schedule and gotten pictures of the big event. Santa Claus had come to town and everybody was happy.

Yet the actor found himself strangely reluctant to leave. Only a half hour earlier he had been scanning the street for a cab; now he was trying to find excuses to stay.

The driver of the portable molecular manufacturer leaned out of the small cab positioned at the front of the machine and scowled at him. "Hey, buddy? You want a ride or not?"

"Yeah," the actor said. "Just give me a minute."

Only one child remained, the little girl who had been the first to step out of the shadows. She held a Raggedy Ann doll in one

hand and a small plush kitten in the other. She looked up at the actor and smiled.

"You'll be back next year, won't you?" she asked. "I really enjoyed meeting you."

The actor looked up at the sky for a moment, but was forced to look down again when the flakes of snow began to lodge in his eyes. "Of course I will be," he told her. "Next year — and the year after that and the year after that and the year after that . . ."

And he meant every word.

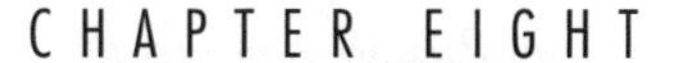

GREEN MACHINES: NANO-TECHNOLOGY AND THE ENVIRONMENT

The thought of going back to Pine Lodge was actually painful. That was what surprised her the most. She had grown up there, in that tiny community in the mountains, and had always remembered it as a place of pristine beauty. Yet when she had returned ten years earlier, it had become ugly. The lake was polluted, the trees were dying, the old stone buildings had been scarred by acid rain. She didn't want to have to see that again. She wanted to retain what few good memories of Pine Lodge she still had.

But her goddaughter was getting married. And she had promised she would attend the wedding. It was not a promise she could get out of easily. So she had packed her overnight bag and bought a train ticket to East Ridge, where she could catch the small bus that ran once a day to Pine Lodge. Now she was crowded into one of the few available seats on a rickety old vehicle wending its way into the mountains, wondering if she'd made the right decision after all.

The first surprise was the sky. The smog she had noticed 10 years earlier, which apparently came from the big city 20 miles away, was nowhere in evidence. She'd heard something about a reduction in smog over the last few years, but she hadn't actually believed it. And the trees looked healthier than she'd ever seen them!

But she still wasn't prepared for Pine Lodge itself. When she stepped off the bus, she caught her breath. The town was beautiful again, every bit as beautiful as she remembered from her childhood. The buildings were unscarred, the lake was lovely in the sunlight, and the pine trees towered over everything just the way they always had.

It was a miracle. But what in the world had caused it?

Technology and nature. These are not, to paraphrase the Beatles, two words that go together well. Technology, in fact, has come to seem antithetical to nature. As the human race has become increasingly technology oriented, so have we moved farther away from the natural world, until it is possible for dwellers in some of the larger cities to live their entire lives without seeing a tree that hasn't been carefully ghettoized into an artificially maintained park.

Not only have we moved farther away from the natural world, but we seem to be destroying that natural world even as we move away from it. In time, there may be no natural world left to go back to. Technology will be all we have.

Is this inevitable? The truth is, it doesn't have to be. In theory, technology and nature can coexist quite peaceably, with one complementing rather than eliminating the other. But in practice, this doesn't seem to be very easy to do. Every time we build a shopping center or a farm, we wind up destroying a piece of grassland or wetlands. Every time a new product rolls off the assembly line in a factory, poisonous chemicals are belched into the atmosphere, destroying a little piece of the air that we breathe. These technologies don't seem to be complementing nature at all. (See Figure 8-1.)

Figure 8-1 These factories may manufacture products that enhance our quality of life, but they certainly aren't enhancing the quality of our atmosphere.

Nanotechnology may change that. Because it allows us to manipulate matter at the level of individual atoms and molecules, nanotechnology will give us greater control over our technology than we've ever had before. And that greater control may not only put an end to pollution and environmental destruction, but give us a tool for cleaning up the damage that's already been done.

UNWANTED BY-PRODUCTS

Nobody wants to pollute. Even the richest, most committed industrialist doesn't like to see black smoke pour out of chimneys. But pollution has come to be seen as the inevitable price of certain aspects of our technology, an unavoidable by-product of the chemical reactions that make modern technology possible.

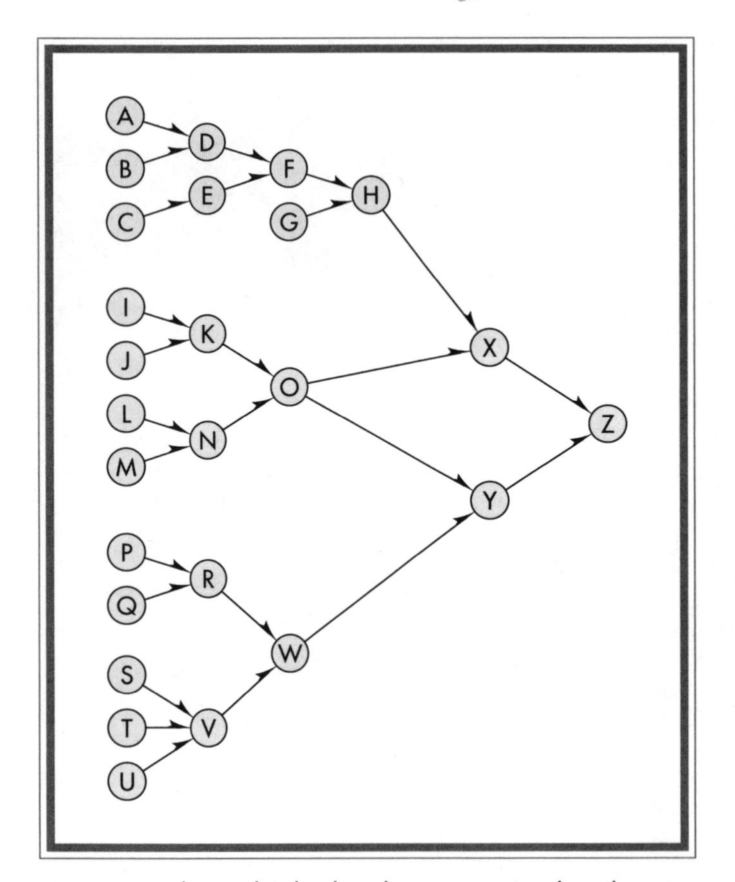

Figure 8-2 Chemical technology has economic value when one chemical can be converted into another chemical of higher value.

Much of our present-day technology is based on chemistry, the conversion of one type of matter into another type of matter. This primarily involves rearranging atoms, converting one molecular structure into another molecular structure. This is worth doing because it's quite possible to convert worthless types of matter into valuable types of matter. Thus, the chemical reactions that perform these conversions are themselves of economic value. (See Figure 8-2.)

Here's how the process works: Add a few quarts of molecule A to a few quarts of molecule B, turn up the heat, and — *voila!* — you have a few quarts of molecule C. Keep doing this enough times, throwing in quarts of chemicals D through Y as needed, and eventually you'll end up with chemical Z, which is what you were after in the first place. Chemical Z may be gasoline or plastic or insecticide. Whatever it is, it has a higher value than chemicals A through Y combined, so it was worth your while to cook it up. You then package chemical Z appropriately, sell it for what the market will bear, and smile all the way to the bank.

If this were all that there was to chemical technology, there would be no problem. The chemist would simply lay his or her magic wand atop chemical A and turn it into chemical Z. The industrialist would make a profit, the public would get a product that it wants, and everybody would be happy.

But chemical reactions don't work that neatly. They tend to produce unwanted by-products. Because these by-products have no economic value — nobody wants to pay money for them and it's too much trouble to turn them into anything useful — they are simply discarded. That's where pollution comes from.

The easiest way to get rid of unwanted chemical by-products is to vent them into the air or dump them in a river. And for many years, that was pretty much what was done. The earth's atmosphere is vast and its oceans are large, and the by-products simply vanished into them, as though they had never existed. (See Figure 8-3.)

Figure 8-3 The easiest way to get rid of unwanted chemical by-products is to dump them into the nearest convenient receptacle.

We have reached the point, however, where this is no longer feasible. There are too many factories producing too many unwanted by-products for the earth's atmosphere and oceans to handle. The quality of the environment is beginning to degrade.

A slightly more expensive solution, but one that is increasingly necessary, is to place these unwanted by-products in designated waste dumps. But even this doesn't always work. So-called toxic wastes, those that represent an active chemical danger to people and animals that come in contact with them, have a way of working their way back into the ecosystem, leaking into the groundwater, and seeping into the atmosphere.

In many instances, further chemical reactions can convert these toxic wastes into nontoxic wastes, or even into useful substances with some economic value. But it's usually either expensive or inconvenient to do so; that's why it wasn't done in the first place. So laws have to be passed to force industry to take care of its own wastes, with fines being imposed to make it more expensive not to convert the wastes than to convert them. Of course, this usually translates into higher costs for the consumer, as the cost of detoxifying by-products becomes part of the cost of creating the chemical product itself.

What impact will nanotechnology have on this economically vicious cycle? In many ways, nanotechnology is a chemical technology. It involves converting one type of matter into another type of matter, by rearranging the structure of molecules. But nanotechnology will be much more precise than existing chemical technologies. A nanoassembler will take molecular fragments and directly create products from them, without passing through the intermediate stages necessary with chemical technology. And it will do this by the direct application of force to specific atoms and molecules, rather than through the random interactions of large numbers of atoms and molecules in an artificially heated soup. As a result, there will be fewer unwanted by-products, perhaps none at all. By and large, nanotechnology will be a nonpolluting technology.

Furthermore, if there are unwanted by-products, it will be relatively easy to do something useful with them. Assemblers work cheaply and they can be made to work efficiently too. If there are raw molecules left over after a nanoproduct has been constructed, they can easily be used for something else, or converted into a storable nontoxic form for later use. When we have control over individual atoms, there's no point in letting those atoms become parts of molecules that will become a liability to society.

Eric Drexler and his wife, Chris Peterson, like to refer to nanotechnology as a "green technology," because it has the potential to produce almost no pollution. Not only can nanotechnology be nonpolluting if used properly, but it can be used to clean up the pollution of the past. In fact, yesterday's pollution may even become tomorrow's valuable resource.

MINING THE AIR

Many of the resources that have value in today's economy will cease to be valuable in a nanotechnological economy. When virtually everything can be made out of a handful of different atoms — atoms that are found in great abundance in the world around us — rarer elements and naturally occurring molecules will no longer be worth the effort required to pull them out of the ground. Nor will it be possible any longer to justify the environmental destruction that results from digging them up.

What will be valuable is carbon. From a molecular point of view, carbon atoms are the most versatile construction material around. They can bond with more atoms in more different ways than any other atom except silicon. This is why carbon atoms are the chief structural element of living organisms. They will be the chief structural elements of nanostructures as well.

In the nanotechnological economy, carbon will have a relatively high value compared to other elements. And where will we find that carbon? Lots of places. One of them is the air itself. We've been pumping it full of carbon for the last 200 years. In fact, you release carbon into the air every time you exhale.

Most of the carbon in the air is in the form of carbon dioxide molecules. Ordinarily, this is not a pollutant. It's a natural component of the atmosphere. Plants need it in order to survive; they "breathe" the stuff. The fraction of the air that is made of carbon dioxide is quite small, less than 1 percent. There was a lot more of it when the earth was young, but primitive plant life absorbed most of it. This is a good thing, since animals (including human beings) don't coexist well with large amounts of it.

In recent decades, the amount of carbon dioxide in the air has begun to increase again. Why? Because of human activity, mostly industrial activity. Whenever carbon-based materials are burned, carbon dioxide is released along with the smoke. Plants do their bit to take this carbon dioxide back out of circulation and the oceans absorb a surprising amount of it — nobody's sure how much — but the overall concentration in the atmosphere seems to be increasing, slowly and surely.

This could have dire consequences. Carbon dioxide is one of the gases responsible for the so-called greenhouse effect, by which the heat of sunlight is trapped in the earth's atmosphere before it can escape back into outer space. Without the greenhouse effect, the earth would be a cold, cold place indeed. But a little bit of greenhouse effect goes a long way. If something were to significantly alter the amount of carbon dioxide in the atmosphere, increasing it or decreasing it, it would also alter the greenhouse effect, which would in turn alter the climatic patterns that we have become accustomed to. While it could be argued that one climatic pattern is as good as another, within a reasonable range of alternatives, any significant changes in climatic patterns would cause wholesale economic disruption in countries that have come to depend on the climatic patterns being the way they are. Crops could die on the vine, season after season. Tourism patterns could be sharply altered. Worse, if the carbon dioxide levels were to increase (producing so-called global warming), the polar icecaps could start to melt and low-lying areas, such as Bangladesh and much of the state of Florida, could vanish entirely beneath the waves. (See Figure 8-4.)

This is a controversial topic, but there are a few pessimistic scientists who believe that we have already set such a pattern of warming irreversibly into effect. And more than a few not-so-pessimistic ones believe that we will soon do so if we keep pumping carbon dioxide into the atmosphere at the rate we have been doing so lately.

Figure 8-4 Will global warming destroy crops and cause Miami to vanish beneath the waves?

What can we do about this? One solution is to stop producing carbon dioxide, but that's more easily said than done. Another, remarkably enough, is to grow trees, which can take the carbon dioxide back out of the air. Whether we can do enough of either of these things soon enough to prevent at least a few significant climatic alterations is an open question.

Nanotechnology offers a third possibility: recycle the carbon dioxide back into valuable products. As its name implies, every molecule of carbon dioxide is made up of two oxygen atoms and one carbon atom. Individually, these are not pollution. Oxygen, in reasonable amounts, is an important component of the atmosphere for human beings; we couldn't breathe (or light a match) without it. And the carbon can be used to build things. In the nanotech world, carbon will be sufficiently valuable that it will be worth extracting it from the air, using nanotechnological filters, and using it again. What it can be used for is to build things. And what can it build? Just about anything.

In the nanotech world of the twenty-first century, almost any form of twentieth-century pollution will have economic value, because that once useless pollution can be broken apart for its component atoms, which in turn can be used as construction materials. And when there's an economic value in doing something, it inevitably will be done. Ironically, the resources that will be turned to cleaning up pollution in the next century will be the same ones that created that pollution in this century.

Nanotechnology will provide the ultimate in recycling. With nanotechnology, almost anything can be recycled into almost anything else.

It was a beautiful wedding. Her goddaughter looked lovely in white. She cried, of course. Doesn't everybody cry at weddings? Afterward, at the reception, she pulled her goddaughter aside for a few moments of private conversation.

"It's so beautiful here!" she said, her voice still filled with the awe she had felt when stepping off the bus. "What happened?"

"Didn't you hear?" her goddaughter asked. "It was those nanotech engineers. They used Pine Lodge as a pilot project for their antipollution equipment."

"I'm afraid I don't keep up with that sort of thing," she admitted. "I don't even know what this nanotech stuff is, though I've seen the term in the newspapers."

..."I don't understand it either," her goddaughter said. "All I know is that they sprinkled some stuff on the lake and — poof! The pollution went away. Took about a week, then things looked good as new. They also sprinkled it in the woods. Said it was a lot of tiny machines."

"Tiny machines?" she said. "That's hard to believe."

"Yes, it is," her goddaughter told her. "But that's what they said."

Tiny machines, eh? She thought about that afterward, as the bus took her back down the mountain to the train. She wasn't sure she believed that part, but it really didn't matter. What counted was that a miracle had occurred.

And it had given her back the Pine Lodge of her youth!

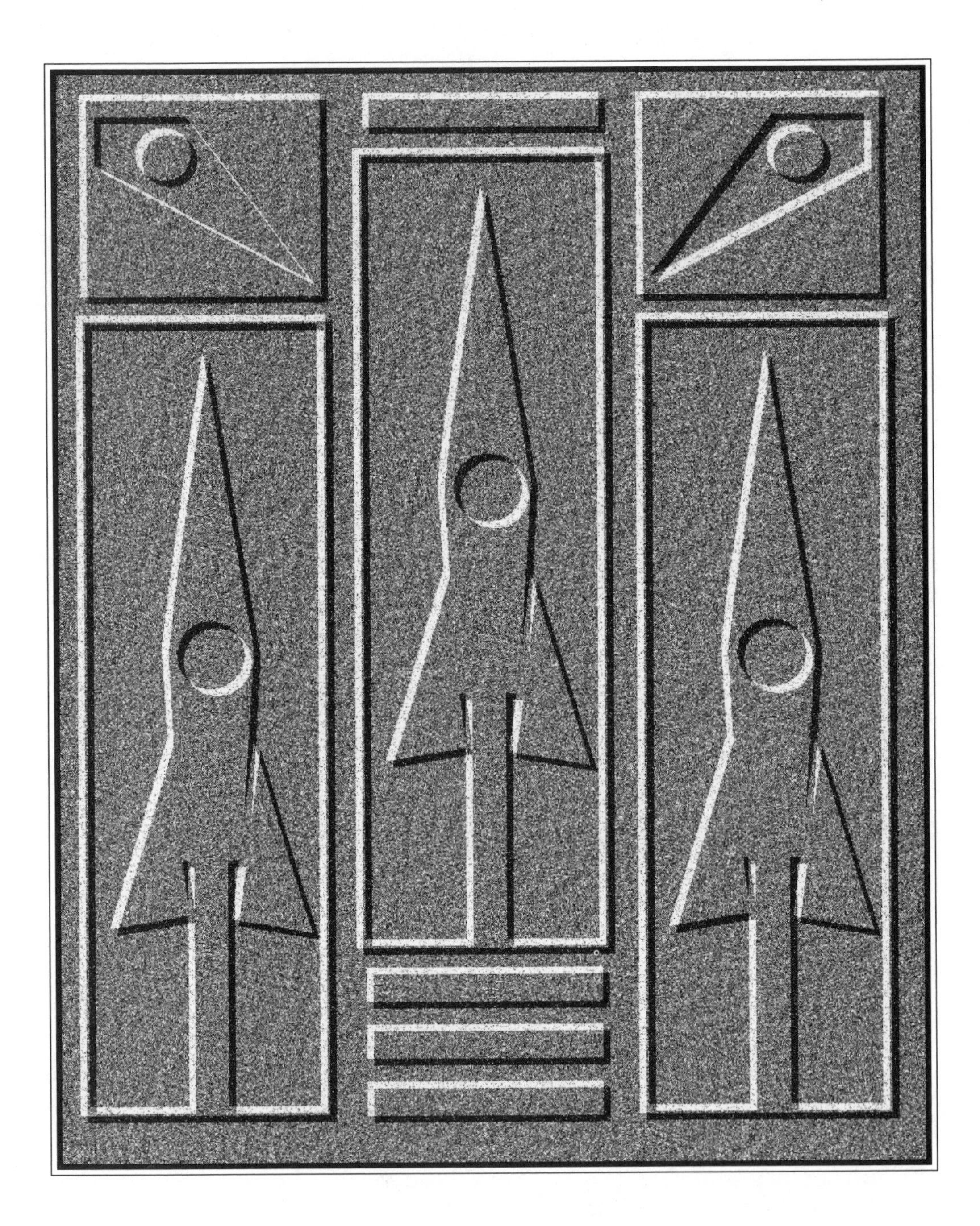

CHAPTER NINE

NANOTECHNOLOGY IN SPACE

"Hello, sailor," said the NASA representative, with a laugh. "How are things on earth?"

The astronaut smiled. "I guess I am a kind of sailor," she said. "I hadn't thought of it that way before. Things back on earth are fine. Or at least they were six hours ago, when I caught the skystalk up here."

She looked around at the interior of the space station. It had been decorated to look like a plushly appointed sitting room from the Victorian era, a style that was all the rage back on Earth. Hard to believe they were at the top of a 35,000-kilometer tall tower with an elevator inside. In the twentieth century, when she had been born, this sort of extravagance would have been unthinkable.

But cheap parts and flawless components had made a big difference. Now there were inexpensive spacecraft and spacesuits thin and flexible as gossamer yet constructed from heat- and radiation-resistant materials similar to diamond. It had given new life to the space program and to the idea that the exploration and habitation of space was somehow a noble goal.

"How do you feel about the big trip?" the NASA representative asked.

"How do you think I feel?" she asked. "Excited as all get out. It's only been ten years since the first manned mission to Mars and now we're on our way to the stars. It's enough to make your head spin. And here I am, right in the middle of it."

"Your ship's almost ready to go," the NASA representative said, motioning the astronaut toward a large rectangular viewport. Through it, she could see the distant constellations glowing like fireflies — except that high above the earth's atmosphere they no longer twinkled. One of these was the star that she'd be heading toward in just a few days. And circling it was a small planet that astronomers had decided had a small probability of being earthlike. If it wasn't, she and the rest of her crew would have a choice. Explore it as best they could, then head back to Earth — or keep on going, exploring the galaxy, for the rest of their lives. Which, in an age of nanotechnological medicine, was going to be a long time.

Almost smack in the middle of the viewport, obscuring a large portion of the galaxy, was the starship. It looked like the sail of a sailboat, but a hundred times larger and gossamer thin. In a few days, when the anchor that tethered the starship to the space station was removed, it would start moving outward toward the edges of the solar system, propelled by the gentle pressure of sunlight and a giant laser beam on the moon that would give them the extra push they needed to reach the stars. And the astronaut would be propelled outward with it, joining a crew of twenty in the attached life support module.

"It's going to be a long trip," said the NASA representative. "Two hundred years. Are you ready for that?"

"I'm ready," the astronaut said, thinking already of strange life forms and alien sunsets. The ship carried a large stock of assemblers. Anything they needed, including the nanomedicine that would keep the crew perpetually young, could be manufactured as they went, from a large store of feedstock molecules that they would keep in the hold. Except for books, of course. But she was taking her own collection of those on optical disk.

She had always wanted a chance to catch up on her reading....

CHAPTER NINE: Nanotechnology in Space

Whatever happened to the exploration of space?

It hasn't gone away. At this writing, the *Galileo* probe was on its way to Jupiter (albeit with a crippled antenna), and several other probes were either being designed or readied for flights to the planets. (See Figure 9-1.) But some of the life has gone out of the space program. The enthusiasm that used to be part of this effort has somehow waned.

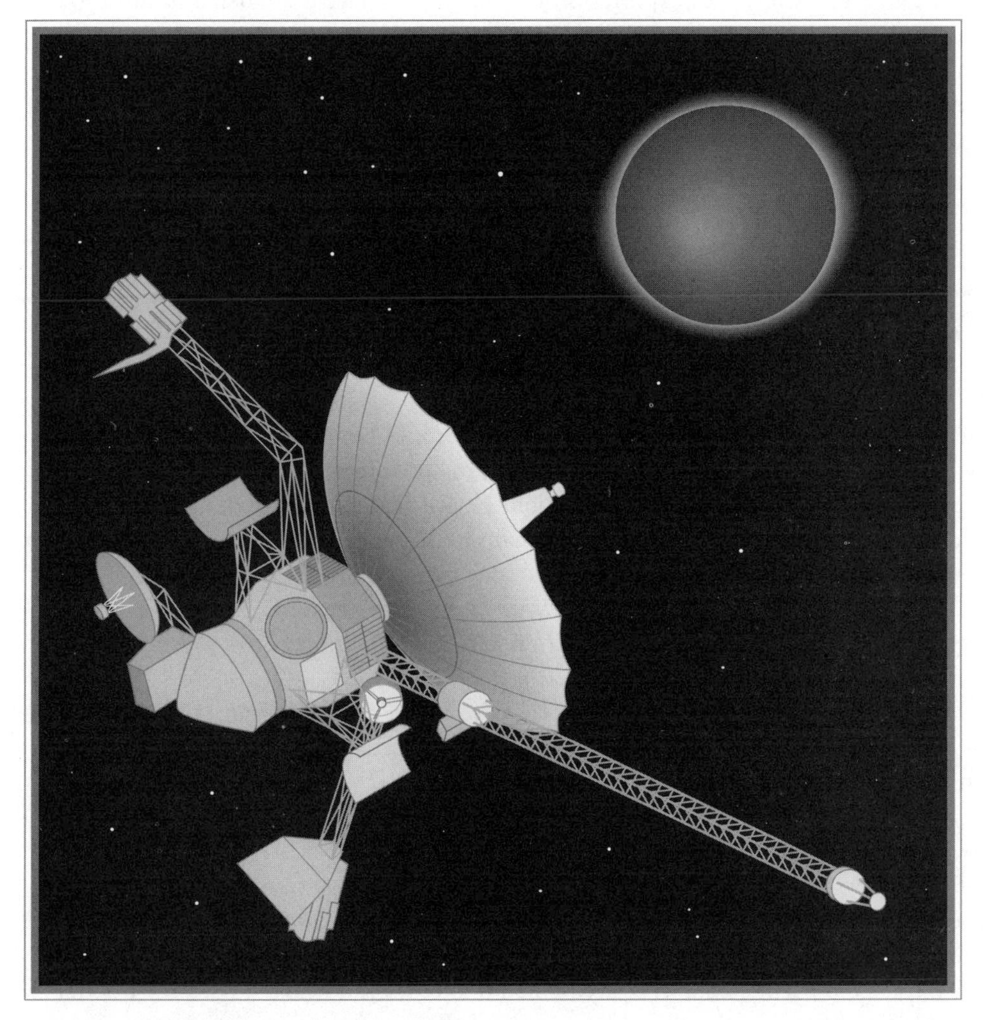

Figure 9-1 The *Galileo* probe on its way to Jupiter.

It's not hard to figure out why. Space exploration has two major drawbacks, and they are significant ones indeed. It is expensive and (in the case of astronaut-controlled spaceflight) it is dangerous. In an age when budgets are tight and even the smallest risks are frowned upon, support for space programs in the United States has been at a low ebb since the early 1970s.

We all know why space exploration is dangerous. Space is a harsh and unforgiving environment, one in which human beings have not evolved to live and in which machinery does not necessarily operate as it does on earth. In order to survive in space, we must manufacture special environments to shut out the vacuum and the cold. To guard against failures, these systems must be precision engineered and heavily redundant.

This is one of the reasons that space exploration is expensive. Wholly automated space probes are cheaper than those that must carry human beings, but they aren't cheap. The truth is, it takes a big wallet to explore the universe beyond earth's atmosphere.

MOLECULAR MANUFACTURING IN ORBIT — AND BEYOND

If the components necessary for space exploration could be manufactured inexpensively yet with a higher degree of quality than current manufacturing techniques allow, a lot of life would reenter the space effort. It might be possible to build space vehicles that wouldn't bust the budgets of entire nations while risking the lives of any passengers they may carry.

As we saw in Chapter 7, high-quality yet inexpensive manufacturing is one of the strong suits of nanotechnology. Could nanotechnology be the key to reaching the planets — and eventually the stars?

Eric Drexler thinks so. A long-time devotee of the space program, the applications of nanotechnology to this effort were one of the reasons he initially became interested in molecular manufacturing.

LIGHT BUT POWERFUL

One of the problems with launching a rocket into orbit is weight. Rockets are heavy. When filled with fuel they are heavier still. Ironically, the heavier the rocket, the more fuel it requires to reach escape velocity, which makes it even heavier. And the heavier both rocket and fuel are, the smaller the payload that they carry into space.

On the other hand, if there were some way to make rockets lighter, they would require less fuel, which would further reduce the final weight of the system. Light rockets would be cheaper to use and could carry a larger payload. But with conventional manufacturing techniques, they would also be flimsier, which isn't necessarily desirable.

With nanotechnological materials, it might be possible to build a rocket out of diamond-like structures that would be light yet incredibly strong. And this means that they could carry larger payloads.

SOLAR SAILS

Nanotechnology may also make new forms of space travel possible. One means of traveling between the planets in our solar system that has been suggested many times but never implemented for technical reasons is the solar sail, a sheet of lightweight material that could be opened in space like the sail of a ship (Figure 9-2). Once opened, the pressure of radiation from the sun could be used to push the sail — and anything attached to it — through space. Since the solar sail is essentially powered by solar energy, which is available in outer space in immense quantities, it would be extremely inexpensive to use. And it would never run out of fuel.

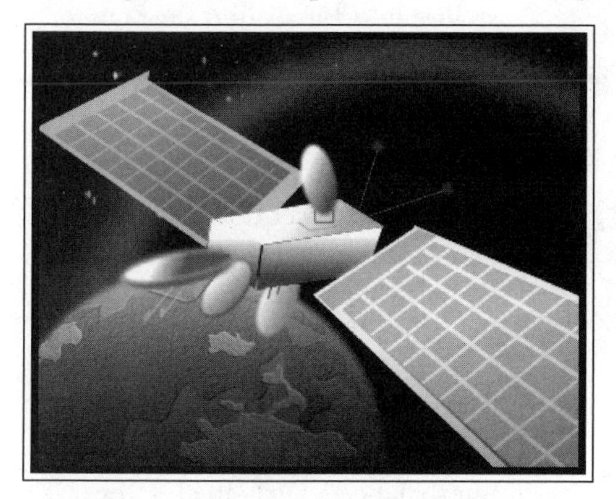

Figure 9-2 A solar sail on its way to the outer reaches of the solar system.

But a solar sail isn't an easy thing to construct. It would need to be extremely thin yet extremely strong, two qualities that don't necessarily go together. Once again, molecular manufacturing methods might be able to manufacture such a device. Eric Drexler suggests that it may be possible to build solar sails only 20 nanometers thick.

SPACE ELEVATORS

Perhaps the most incredible suggestion that anyone has yet made for launching space vehicles (one that would benefit from molecular manufacturing processes) is the space

Figure 9-3 A space elevator at work.

elevator. (For a fictional treatment of this concept, see Arthur C. Clarke's novel *The Fountains of Paradise.*) The space elevator would be, in effect, a satellite that has been tethered to the ground.

When orbiting the earth at approximately 35,000 kilometers, a satellite is said to be in geosynchronous orbit. Because it is orbiting the earth at exactly the same speed that the earth revolves on its axes, such a satellite in orbit around the equator appears to hang motionless in space, always remaining above the same point on the earth's surface. Theoretically, it would be possible to build an immense tower downward from such a satellite, all the way to the ground. By placing an elevator-like device inside the tower, it would then be possible to travel up and down from the satellite at will, without a rocket or any need for achieving escape velocity (Figure 9-3). Properly counterbalanced, such an elevator would use relatively little power.

What good would this do us? Satellites could be carried to the top in the elevator and released. Similarly, planetary probes could be released from the top of the tower in such a way that the earth's rotation would push them outward into interplanetary space. In theory, this would be cheaper than launching satellites and probes with conventional chemical rockets.

But such a space elevator would not only be fabulously expensive; it would be quite beyond current manufacturing techniques. Could nanotechnology make it affordable? That's impossible to say at present: but with molecular manufacturing techniques at our disposal, projects that may have seemed miraculous in the twentieth century may seem like business as usual in the twenty-first.

...The astronaut looked through the viewing monitor at the surface of Shiva. The crew had named the planet after Shiva the Destroyer, of Hindu legend, because it had destroyed every probe that they had sent down to its surface. As far as they had been able to tell, the surface temperature of Shiva was in excess of 800 degrees Kelvin and its atmospheric pressure was more than 100 times that of earth.

She turned to the captain. "It's hell down there. Worse than Venus."

"Yeah," said the captain with a laugh. "I wish the astronomer who called this planet 'earthlike' could be here to see this. We could send him down in the next probe."

The astronaut sighed. "Looks like we won't be colonizing after all."

"We wouldn't survive down there for ten seconds," the captain said. "Not for ten nanoseconds."

"So," the astronaut said. "What do we do now? Go home? Go back to earth?"

"We can't decide that unilaterally," the captain said. "We'll have to put it up to a vote of the crew."

The astronaut smiled. Just above the captain's head was a viewport made of thin diamondoid glass. Through it, she could see the stars.

"We don't have to," she said. "We both know what they'll say."

"Onward?" the captain said.

"That's right," the astronaut replied. "Onward." She gestured toward the viewport. "To the stars."

CHAPTER TEN

THE GLORIOUS NANOFUTURE: WHAT'S THE CATCH?

The worst part was the voices in his head. They had begun two nights earlier. He had considered telling the sergeant about them, but had decided not to. He didn't want anybody to think he was crazy.

What really bothered him was what the voices were saying. They were telling him to betray his own buddies, the soldiers in his platoon. One of the voices had even told him he should kill his friends. Grab a gun and shoot everybody in the barracks, it had said. Another voice told him he should make a run for it, head across the enemy lines, and surrender to the other side.

You'll be well taken care of, the voice said. You'll be much happier on the other side. The funny thing was, he was starting to believe it.

It had started, he realized, when that thick cloud of black dust had blown in from enemy territory. The other guys had made it back to the barracks in time, but he'd gotten a lungful of the stuff. And now he was beginning to wonder if there hadn't been something strange in that cloud, something that had gotten inside his brain. Something that made him want to do terrible things . . .

He picked up his rifle and began fingering the trigger. Just fire the gun, the voice told him. Just fire the gun and you'll feel a lot better.

Go on over, the other voice said to him. Go on over to the other side. You'll be much happier there.

His finger began to tighten on the trigger . . .

"Got him!" cried a voice from behind his left ear. He felt strong hands close around his neck and someone deftly lifted the gun from his grasp. "He's a berserker! Somebody gave him a dose of nanodust!"

A man in a crisply starched uniform walked up to him and held a small device up to his head. It made a faint clicking sound. "You're right," the man said. "I register the presence of some kind of nanocircuitry inside his brain. Looks like we caught him just in time!"...

So far, nanotechnology sounds too good to be true. And we all know that when something sounds too good to be true, there's got to be a catch. Either it isn't really true, or it isn't all that good. Or both.

What's the catch with nanotechnology? Could it be that everything we've talked about in this book will turn out to be just so much pie in the sky, a pretty picture with no correspondence to reality? Or is there going to be an unexpected downside, a dark and deadly cloud lurking somewhere behind the glorious silver lining?

These are important questions, and it's impossible to write a book about nanotechnology without dealing with them. Indeed, it's quite important that they be dealt with — now, while nanotechnology is still on the drawing board. If nanotechnology is just pie in the sky, then we don't want to waste our resources trying to make it work when we could be expending our energy on more important matters. And if it will have serious drawbacks, we should be prepared for them before they arrive.

In this chapter, we'll examine both of these questions. First, we'll talk about whether nanotechnology is going to be possible at all. Then we'll talk about the downside — the potential abuses of nanotechnology.

IS NANOTECHNOLOGY POSSIBLE?

As we've made perfectly clear in the first eight chapters of this book, nanotechnology does not exist. It's possible that it may never exist. However, history has demonstrated that if a technology is both technically feasible and of economic value, it will eventually come into being. Nanotechnology is certainly of economic value. So the only thing that will stop it from coming into existence are the laws of the universe. It may simply not be possible.

In technology as in science, it is difficult to prove that something cannot be done. Science offers few absolute barriers to human endeavor. Einstein's speed-of-light barrier is one. (See Figure 10-1.) Heisenberg's uncertainty principle is another. Gödel's incompleteness theorem is a third. But there are ways to get around even these "absolute barriers." Serious theorists have suggested ever more science-fictional sounding ways of evading the speed-of-light barrier, such as tachyons and cosmic wormholes. Physicists have plumbed ever deeper into the ultimate nature of energy and matter, despite the daunting spectre of quantum uncertainty. And Gödel has not discouraged generations of mathematicians from devising ever more arcane logical systems, incomplete though they must always be.

Figure 10-1 The speed-of-light barrier is one of the few absolute limits that the universe places on human endeavor. But could there be a way around it?

So, paradoxically, it may be impossible to say that nanotechnology is impossible. Up until now, in fact, we have assumed it to be *quite* possible. Certainly, this is the opinion of Eric Drexler, and of the various people involved in one way or another with his Foresight Institute. But not everyone concurs. There are those who believe that nanotechnology simply isn't feasible, at least not in the form that Drexler foresees and in the time frame he has in mind.

Some scientists, such as the redoubtable AI pioneer Marvin Minsky of MIT, have backed Drexler wholeheartedly. But many others have taken a wait-and-see attitude, preferring not to commit one way or another. A few have gone even further; Philip Barth, an engineer at the Hewlett-Packard Company, is quoted in *Science* magazine as calling Drexler a "flake." (Drexler has challenged him to present a more scientific — and less *ad hominem* — criticism.) And other scientists and engineers have expressed doubts about his vision of the future.

Drexler suggests that they just haven't listened closely enough to what he has to say. This is quite possibly the case, since he has had a great deal to say on the subject, much of it in print, and most scientists have little time for reading outside their fields. Alas, Drexler's work falls outside just about *everybody's* fields, since nanotechnology is an interdisciplinary discipline (a neatly oxymoronic term), which borrows a little bit from everybody but belongs to just about nobody.

Still, some scientists have gone head-to-head with Drexler, making specific objections to the way in which he believes nanotechnology will progress. A telling exchange between Drexler and reporter/chemist Simson Garfinkel occurs in the Summer 1990 issue of the *Whole Earth Review.* The latter sets forth a number of antinanotechnology arguments. Most of the serious ones have to do with the workings of the universal assembler: how it will be able to sense and manipulate atoms, for instance. Drexler argues that most of Garfinkel's arguments are simply engineering difficulties that can be overcome with sufficient pluck and ingenuity; he even suggests solutions to some of them. Garfinkel never effectively answers these points.

In order to persuade more people that there is substance behind the flash of nanotech, Drexler's Foresight Institute has sponsored a series of nanotechnology conferences, some specifically for scientists, others for the general public. And he has written a book, *Nanosystems: Molecular Machinery, Manufacturing and Computation,* that sets forth an extensive analysis of nanotechnology in stupefying technical detail. Although nearly inaccessible to the lay reader, the book certainly makes Drexler's point: he has given this subject a *great* deal of thought. And he is able to express those thoughts in a concrete form that can be criticized by other scientists. Whether it will be criticized, and how effective that potential criticism will be, was unknown at the time of this writing.

In the end, the only way to prove that nanotechnology is possible is to make it happen. And the only way to prove that it isn't possible is to wait and see if it doesn't happen. Although it would be a shame if we end up wasting valuable resources on a technology that ultimately isn't feasible, it would be even worse if we *fail* to develop nanotechnology because we *didn't* devote enough resources to it.

Because if the right people don't develop nanotechnology, the wrong people just might.

THE DARK SIDE OF THE FORCE

There is no technology so benevolent that it cannot be abused. And the more powerful a technology is, the more horrible are the ways in which it can be abused. Nanotechnology has the potential to be a powerful technology indeed. And so the potential for abuse is also great.

Eric Drexler has done a great deal of thinking about that potential. It is his contention — and it is difficult to argue with this — that the best time to think about the abuse of nanotechnology is now, while there is still no nanotechnology to be abused. Because if we wait until the first assemblers are in existence, and the first nanotech products are rolling off the assembly line, it might be too late.

As with any technology, nanotechnology can be abused in two different ways. The first is deliberate abuse, by those who want to use nanotechnology for selfish or vicious ends. The second is inadvertant abuse, by well-meaning nanotechnologists who have not fully thought through the uses to which they are putting their shiny new tool. We'll talk about both of these in turn, beginning with deliberate abuse.

NANOWAR AND NANOTERROR

One of the oldest uses of human technology is war. In fact, war is one of the single greatest driving forces behind technological development. During almost every war, technology takes a quantum jump, as society pours immense economic resources into the war machine and the war machine in turn uses those resources to build ever more advanced weapons.

Imagine what nanotechnology could mean in a time of war. Weapons too small to see. Weapons that can enter the bodies of enemy soldiers and kill them from the inside out. Weapons that can evade any known means of electronic detection.

Of course, in one sense such nanoweapons are no different from the chemical and biological weapons of wars past and present. But chemical and biological weapons aren't intelligent. They don't have tiny computers inside them, directing them to their targets with unerring accuracy. Nanoweapons are like chemical and biological weapons, only more so. In a way, this may be good. Nanoweapons could be programmed not to harm innocent bystanders, only the soldiers themselves — a small blessing, but a blessing nonetheless.

But this same programmability has terrifying uses in the wrong hands. Terrorists could program nanoweapons to attack only their enemies, turning a weapon that might otherwise be too horrible to use into a weapon that no zealous terrorist could resist. Bigots might use nanoweapons to attack only members of a certain race or a certain religion. Dictators might use nanoweapons to attack only those who cast their votes incorrectly or speak harshly about the current regime, even in private.

Of course, we have lived with possibilities as horrible as these for most of the twentieth century, and somehow we have survived. Surely nuclear weaponry has a potential for abuse as great as any nanomachine, and we have managed to live with that potential for nearly half a century. And the bomb was created with almost no safeguards against its abuse, except for the absolute secrecy surrounding its existence — secrecy that was blown into atoms when the first small atom bomb was dropped on Hiroshima in 1945. Similarly, chemical warfare technologies have been around since at least World War I, and no terrorist has yet managed to abuse them in a significant way, though the possibility is always there. (See Figure 10-2.)

Figure 10-2 Nanomachines have much the same potential for abuse as nuclear weapons. We've learned to live with one. Can we live with the other?

Eric Drexler feels that we should have safeguards in place against the deliberate abuse of nanotechnology from the beginning. He suggests that we make special-purpose nanoassemblers available to anyone who wants to use them, but that we make the tools for nanodesign — the creation of brand new, experimental nanotechnological devices — available only to a licensed few. That way, anyone can make nanomachines, but those nanomachines that could be abused by terrorists will not be allowed into general circulation.

That still leaves open the possibility of nanowarfare by governments themselves, but that's a possibility we may just have to live with, the way that we have lived with the possibility of governments abusing thermonuclear, chemical, and biological warfare. Somehow, we have survived.

WELL-MEANING ACCIDENTS

The other possibility is that nanotechnology will be abused quite accidentally, by those who intend to use it responsibly. Perhaps a well-meaning scientist will design a nanomachine that performs some benevolent task inside the human body, but under certain conditions the software that controls the nanomachine will go berserk. Anyone who has used computer programs knows that they are prone to sudden, catastrophic failure. Program bugs can lurk in even the best-written computer software, waiting to be triggered when an unexpected condition is encountered. What if such a bug were to turn a benevolent nanomachine into a vicious killer — after it was already inside the body of an unsuspecting human?

Or what if a nanomachine that performed some potentially dangerous task, such as destroying waste, somehow found itself in a situation that it was not equipped to handle — and began destroying homes, cars, even people, in the same manner that it normally destroyed waste? Of course, such a device would have safeguards in place to keep it from operating outside of its predetermined boundary conditions — but what if those safeguards failed?

Although these possibilities are frightening, neither is particularly likely to happen. The first case seems probable simply because software failures have proved to be so common in present-day technology. Yet methods are being developed even now for guaranteeing that software failures are few and far between. And even if these methods don't work as well as we'd like, few if any software failures result in a piece of software going berserk. In fact, almost every major software failure has precisely the same result: system crash. The system simply stops working. The worst thing that's likely to happen to a nanomachine with a bad program is that it will drop dead. If it happens to be in a human body at the time, it will probably be flushed out by the kidneys

and deposited where most useless molecules from the body go eventually — in the sewers.

As for the second scenario, it's unlikely that anybody would design a nanomachine that would perform a potentially dangerous task such as destroying waste in a manner that would also be dangerous in other situations. More likely, if such a machine were to somehow escape from its task of destroying waste, it would find itself incapable of doing much of anything at all, and would go the way of the nanomachine with the software failure.

Still, the possibility of inadvertant nanotechnology abuse — nanotech accidents, if you will — is one that should be seriously studied. If we think about these possibilities now, while we still have room to do so with some leisure, we may not have to worry about them quite so much when nanotechnology actually exists — and they can really happen.

BRAVE NEW WORLD

Even if nanotechnology isn't abused, or if we find ways to contain that abuse, it will bring about serious changes in our society. The end of disease alone, implying as it does the end of aging as well, has serious implications for the future. What will we do if people stop dying? As much as we detest death, it is necessary to keep the population balance intact. If nobody dies, how do we find room for the next generation? And the generation after that, and after that, and after that?

These are serious questions, which deserve more space than we can give them here. Suffice it to say that in a nanotechnological world, people will have to change the way they live. Having children may be a luxury that few will be able to afford, until some way is found to increase the available living space. And what are some of the ways in which that might be done? Who knows? Technology has opened new ways of living in the past and almost certainly it will do so again in the future. Drexler has suggested that we may want to put our resources into space colonization, so that the terrestrial life forms can expand off of the planet in much the same way that they have expanded *on* the planet up until now.

Of course, this might not be feasible. But it is the sort of solution that must be given a second look if nanotechnology alters the very way in which human beings live — and die.

...Considering that he had been on the verge of shooting them all, everybody was quite nice to him. In the infirmary, the doctors gave him a dose of some kind of liquid that made the voices go away. And a very nice woman came to talk with him. What she told him was that he wasn't crazy. The enemy had simply put some sort of tiny computers into his head, each of them no larger than a grain of dust. In fact, they had probably been contained in the dust he had breathed a few days before.

"That's pretty scary," he said. "If the enemy can make our own soldiers shoot their buddies and defect to the other side, then we're in a lot of trouble. You can't fight tiny little computers with rifles."

"You're quite right," the woman said. "That's why we've developed machines for detecting the tiny computers. So far, we've managed to track down everybody who breathed the nanodust."

"Well, that makes me feel a lot better," he said. "Of course, if the enemy ever finds a way to make tiny little computers that we can't detect with those machines, we'll still be in a lot of trouble."

"That's right, too," she said. To his surprise, he noticed that she was holding a pistol in her hand. And she was pointing it straight at him. "In fact, the voices in my head tell me that's exactly what they've done."

He started to ask her what else the voices in her head had told her. But it was too late.

She had already pulled the trigger.

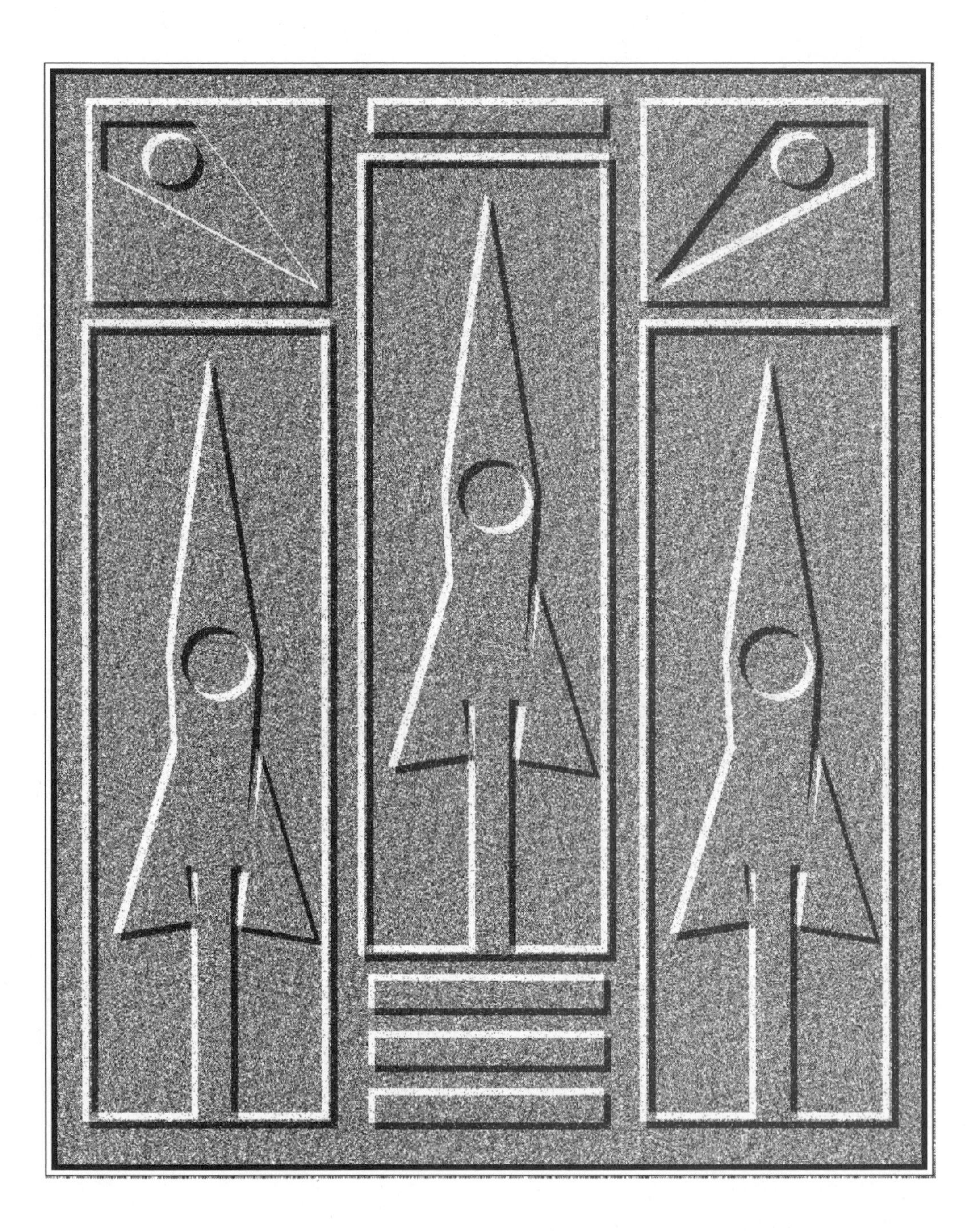

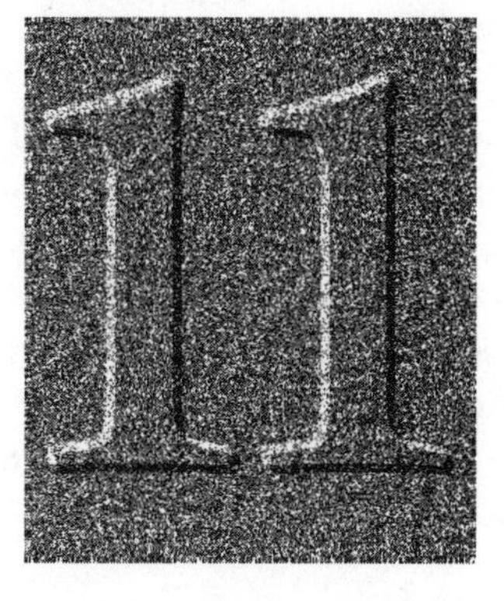

HOW CLOSE ARE WE NOW? NANOTECHNOLOGY IN THE 1990S

So how far away is all of this? Are the miracles described in this book just around the corner, or are they centuries away?

It has been said, with some wisdom, that a prophet should never be too specific, especially when it comes to dates. When you say that something is going to happen in five years and it doesn't, you'll be roundly castigated for being wrong — even if it actually does happen in the sixth year.

Fortunately, I'm not a prophet, so I have no fear of rushing in where angels fear to tread. Nonetheless, it's hard to pin down a precise date for the advent of nanotechnology. Technological advances as dramatic as this rarely arrive on a precise schedule. Thus, the advent of nanotechnology could come any time in the next century — or it might never come at all (see Chapter 9).

However, when Eric Drexler's first popular work on nanotechnology (*Engines of Creation*) appeared in 1986, the figure commonly cited for the arrival of the first nanoassembler was 30 years. (Mind you, this figure does not necessarily come from Drexler himself, and was not used in his book.) If those figures are correct, nanotechnology may be barely more than 20 years away.

Are there indications that nanotechnology is any closer than that? Not really. To the best of my knowledge, no one has yet begun constructing an actual assembler, though plans for it are on several drawing boards. However, a number of current technologies are drawing ever closer to the precise molecular control needed to build the first assembler. And the Japanese government has announced a major project to develop nanotechnological capability.

PROTO-NANOTECHNOLOGY

Earlier, we stated that there are three crude forms of nanotechnology already in existence. These are biotechnology, chemistry, and the precise atomic positioning capabilities offered by atomic force microscopes and other proximal probe devices. We looked at these possibilities in some detail in Chapter 3. Is there any evidence that these technologies really have achieved the capacity to build the first assembler?

Yes, there is. In November 1992, Eric Drexler's Foresight Institute sponsored a conference of scientists and engineers from a number of disciplines, including physics, chemistry, biotechnology, computer science, and engineering, to speak on nanotechnology-related topics and listen to what others had to say on the subject. Speakers from all three of the "proto-nanotechnology" fields were there, and agreed that the precise atomic positioning required for building an assembler is already technically feasible, especially through the use of atomic force microscopes and protein engineering.

Although these capabilities have yet to be put to work building an assembler, Drexler and others have been actively designing molecular components that may be used in the construction of assemblers and other nanomachines. (See Chapter 4 for examples.) Designing molecular machines an atom at a time is a tedious task, however, so many nanodesigners have turned to another tool of modern technology — the computer — for assistance. Software is currently available for both the Macintosh and IBM-compatible microcomputers that can be used for constructing molecular models and simulating the activity of molecular-scale machines. Nanodesigners with programming talent have even turned to writing their own custom molecular design software: a recent issue of *Foresight Update*, the newsletter of Eric Drexler's Foresight Institute, reports on an 800-line program written in the C programming language that generates tubular molecular structures that could be used as nanocomponents. This program was written by researchers at the Xerox Palo Alto Research Center (PARC), which has been the source of much innovative software technology over the last two decades.

Xerox PARC is not the only corporate research entity that has expressed interest in the potential of nanotechnology. John Walker, founder of Autodesk (known both for computer-aided design programs and science-related educational tools), has expressed a substantial commitment to nanotechnology-related software. In 1991, a group of researchers from several different companies, as well as the Foresight Institute, banded together in Palo Alto, California, to form the Institute for Molecular Manufacturing (IMM), an organization dedicated to the development of nanotechnology.

GOVERNMENTAL INTEREST

Given the potential impact that nanotechnology could have on society, both for good and ill, one would expect substantial interest from government bodies in this technology. In the United States, however, this has yet to happen. In the summer of 1992, Eric Drexler testified in front of the U.S. Senate Committee on Commerce, Science, and Transportation's Subcommittee on Science, Technology, and Space as part of a hearing on "New Technologies for a Sustainable World." (The text of this speech is available from the Foresight Institute, at the address given in the Bibliography at the end of this book.) So far, however, Drexler's comments on nanotechnology have had relatively little effect on government policy (though the Congressional Office of Technology Assessment has at least one staff member studying the general field of miniaturized technology).

In Japan, the picture is quite different. At least two major entities within the Japanese government — the Ministry of International Trade and Industry (MITI) and the Science and Technology Agency (STA) — have begun competing programs for creating small-scale technology. MITI initially focused on what is called the top down approach to this technology, building smaller and smaller machines in a manner similar to that advocated more than 30 years ago by Richard Feynman. STA, by contrast, chose the bottom up approach from the start — direct control of molecules to build nanomachines. Several researchers are now receiving extensive funding from the STA's Exploratory Research for Advanced Technology (ERATO) program to study molecular manufacturing and related topics. Given Japan's success in the past with crash technology development programs, this may indicate that the first assembler will arrive in much less than 30 years, and perhaps less than a decade.

In the meantime, microscale technology is positively thriving. Gears and even motors roughly an order of magnitude smaller than an ant have been developed. Because they are on roughly the same scale as the components of a microchip, machines based on these microscale devices may soon be incorporated into electronic hardware, including computers. But this technology is still several orders of magnitude larger than nanotechnology, and the techniques used to scale machinery down to this size are not applicable on the molecular scale.

So what does this add up to? Are we on the verge of nanotechnology? Or will those last few orders of magnitude (which may or may not have to be traversed, depending on whether nanotechnology is achieved through the top down or the bottom up approach) take many decades to traverse?

Or will it simply not happen at all?

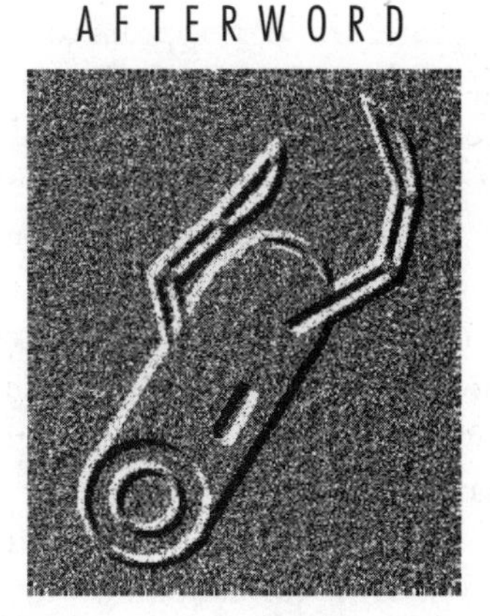

AFTERWORD: THE NANOTECHNOLOGICAL WORLD . . . AND BEYOND

If nanotechnology is realized in its almost pure form — if Eric Drexler's assembler turns out to be tomorrow's reality, and we gain the ability to build virtually anything we want out of a handful of different atoms — it's not hard to guess the sort of benefits that will accrue to a grateful world. It will mean the end of disease and almost the end of death. (Everyone will die sooner or later, and some will choose to do so sooner, but almost everybody will have the option of living for centuries if not for thousands of years.) World hunger will be a thing of the past when food can be conjured directly from dirt, without the need for an intervening layer of agriculture. Lifestyles now accessible only to the wealthy will be available to nearly everyone.

Looked at in this way, nanotechnology appears to be something of a panacea. It will cure all of the problems faced by humanity in the twentieth century. (Well, almost all. There's no obvious nanotechnological cure for our inhumanity to each other, but at least in a nanotechnological world we'll have nothing to blame for our problems but ourselves.) In fact, this would seem to be the major reason for *not* believing in nanotechnology. We all know that panaceas never pan out. Nuclear energy, for instance, was touted at one time as solving all of humankind's energy woes, but where is the nuclear industry today? (It should be noted, however, that the touting was done mostly by public relations people, not the scientists and engineers themselves, who recognized many of the difficulties that lay ahead.)

Yet panaceas do happen. The world *does* change. But human memory is short. Every time the world is altered in some fundamental way, our recollections of what the world was like before the change vanish quickly, as a new generation grows up taking the change for granted. Thus, few people remember a time when the average human life expectancy was less than 40 years and more people died of infected wounds than of cancer, yet both of these things were true in the early years of the twentieth century. And a world without telephones, radio, and television would be alien to most of us, yet all of these things were invented in the last 125 years, a mere eyeblink in the history of humanity. The microcomputer, so essential now in business and in the sciences, is less than a quarter of a century old.

Yes, you say, but preventing infected wounds is trivial; you merely have to keep them sterile. And telephones, radio, and television are based on simple electronic principles. These weren't *hard* problems, like curing cancer or ending world hunger.

But curing cancer and ending world hunger are only hard problems because they haven't been solved yet. In a nanotech world, people will take cures for cancer and the absence of world hunger as much for granted as we take antisepsis. "Cure for cancer?" the technophile of the twenty-first century might say. "World hunger? Sure, but those were easy problems. They only took nanotechnology to cure. And nanotechnology was inevitable."

Which is how it will look — after it happens.

And what will happen after nanotechnology (assuming, once again, that there turns out to be no fundamental reason why nanotechnology itself isn't possible)? That's a tough question. Just deducing the future of the nanotech world is difficult enough without trying to guess what lies beyond it. Will there be a *picotechnology*, a technology that can control entities even smaller than atoms themselves?

It could be, but we can't even begin to guess today how such a technology would work — or why we would want it to. Once we set our sights lower than the size of the atom, we enter a world where things are very different from the world that engineers have come to know and love (or at least to manipulate to profitable ends). We enter the world of quantum mechanics, where matter takes on the nature of waves, and properties such as position and momentum become oddly statistical in nature. Controlling this world, where the size scale is so small that the primary entities are smaller in relation to the atom than the atom is in relation to an elephant, would be nothing like controlling the gears and pistons with which we are familiar. It's impossible to envision a machine constructed from individual electrons, or quarks. Such a notion may not even have meaning.

Eric Drexler has suggested that postnanotechnology technology may not even be the product of human minds, at least not the kind that we are accustomed to dealing with (or to having inside our heads). In Chapter 5, we briefly mentioned Drexler's proposal for reverse engineering the human brain. This might be done using a nanotechnological device that Drexler terms the *disassembler.* Instead of putting things together, the disassembler — as its name certainly implies — would take them apart to see what makes them tick. By taking a human brain apart, we can then build it again from the ground up, using molecular parts. The result could well be a working human brain only a tiny fraction as large as the real thing. Hundreds or even thousands of these brains could then be networked together to form a superbrain, which would be a lot sharper at directing research, devising theories, and developing technology than a real human being could ever be. These superbrains could discover in a decade all of the technology that humans might devise in centuries or millennia.

These superbrains might discover picotechnology, if such a thing is possible. They might even discover the solution to all of the problems that will inevitably be created by nanotechnology. For, far from being a panacea, nanotechnology will doubtlessly introduce far more more problems than it will cure. But if human beings can't find their own way out of these problems, maybe the superbrains can.

And perhaps they will lead us places that the merely human brains that will develop nanotechnology could never imagine.

INDEX

Index

Environmental Awareness

Books have a substantial influence on the destruction of the forests of the Earth. For example, it takes 17 trees to produce one ton of paper. A first printing of 30,000 copies of a typical 480-page book consumes 108,000 pounds of paper which will require 918 trees!

Waite Group Press™ is against the clear-cutting of forests and supports reforestation of the Pacific Northwest of the United States and Canada, where most of this paper comes from. As a publisher with several hundred thousand books sold each year, we feel an obligation to give back to the planet. We will therefore support and contribute a percentage of our proceeds to organizations which seek to preserve the forests of planet Earth.

ARTIFICIAL LIFE PLAYHOUSE

Evolution at Your Fingertips

Stephen Prata

"A fun approach to answering the age-old question: What is Life? **Artificial Life Playhouse** turns your PC into a full blown laboratory, and best-selling author Stephen Prata makes it easy to understand the concepts at work. Watch cellular automata grow into colorful biomorphs, see a mob of protozoa become a society of efficient bacteria foragers, evolve a random phrase into intelligent text. The programs on the bundled disk allow you to experiment with various Wet-Life concepts such as cumulative selection, emergent behavior, mutation, competition systems, and more. Now you can finally take charge of your life...your artificial life, that is.

ISBN: 1-878739-32-8 180 pages, 1 5.25" disk, $23.95 Available now

VIRTUAL REALITY PLAYHOUSE

Nick Lavroff

Jack-in to the world of Virtual Reality with this playful new book and disk package. Virtual Reality is a new interactive technology which creates the convincing illusion that you are completely immersed in worlds existing only inside your computer. **Virtual Reality Playhouse** lets you enter those worlds and even create your own personal digital dimension. Expand the parameters of your mind as you move rapidly from an introduction of virtual reality's basic concepts to visual explorations illustrating real-life applications. Demo programs include a 3-D simulation that puts you inside a robot which travels through a computer-generated city. Or, you can play a game in a 3-D room that can be tilted, spun, and twisted in near impossible ways. Put on the enclosed 3-D glasses and jump right into any one of 8 startling VR simulations. There are even plans for building your own LCD shuttering VR glasses and power glove to manipulate objects in a VR world. For MS/PC DOS machines.

ISBN 1-878739-19-0, 146 pages, 1 3.5" disk, 3-D Glasses, $23.95 Available now

MULTIMEDIA CREATIONS

Hands-On Workshop for Exploring Animation and Sound

Philip Shaddock

Contemplating the jump into multimedia? Do it with **Multimedia Creations** and its powerful bundled GRASP program. Whether novice or programmer, you can create your own animated interactive audio-visual programs: from concept through post production, renderings to video tape. After a brief primer on PC video systems and animation fundamentals, you can start working with GRASP, creating everything from educational programs to your own multimedia cartoons. Work through the entire book/disk package to learn tricks like windowing, color cycling, sprite animation, delta compression techniques, and classical flipbook-style animation. And there are advanced chapters with in-depth coverage and reference sources for power users. Accompanying shareware programs provide you with the basic tools for creating complete multimedia presentations on the PC. For MS/PC DOS machines.

ISBN 1-878739-26-3, 450 pages, 2 5.25" disks, $44.95 Available now

Send for our unique catalog to get more information about these books, as well as our other outstanding and award-winning programming titles, including:

Master C: Let the PC Teach You C and **Master C++: Let the PC Teach You Object-Oriented Programming:** Both book/disk software packages turn your computer into an infinitely patient C and C++ professor.

Workout C: Hundreds of C projects and exercises and a full-featured compiler make this an unbeatable training program and value.

Ray Tracing: "With the **Ray Tracing Creations** book/disk package, you can immediately begin rendering perfect graphic objects like the ones in computer movies. Using the bundled POV-Ray shareware program, you'll learn to control the location, shape, light, shading, and surface texture of 3-D objects you design."

Falcon 3: The Complete Handbook: "Designed for use with Spectrum Holobyte's *Falcon 3* flight simulator, this book and disk combo provide you with training, tips, and tools that will take you from the fundamentals of flight to mastery of theatre command."

Fractals for Windows: "Create, control, and explore fascinating fractals with this book/disk package. Fractals for Windows bundles WINFRACT, a Windows-based program that computes mind-bending fractals faster than lightning and allows you to create fractals of your own. Use zoom boxes, menus, and a mouse to investigate over 85 different fractal types. 3-D glasses are also included."

Image Lab: This unique book/disk set is a complete PC-based "digital darkroom" that covers virtually all areas of graphic processing and manipulation.

WAITE GROUP PRESS™

Satisfaction Report Card

Please fill out this card if you wish to know of future updates to *Nanotechnology Playhouse*, or to receive our catalog.

Company Name: ______________________

Division/Department ______________ **Mail Stop:** ______________

Last Name: ______________ **First Name:** ______________ **Middle Initial:** ______

Street Address: ______________________

City: ______________ **State:** ______________ **Zip:** ______

Daytime telephone: ( ) ______________________

Date product was acquired: Month ______ **Day** ______ **Year** ______ **Your Occupation:** ______________

Overall, how would you rate this Nanotechnology Playhouse?

- ☐ Excellent
- ☐ Very Good
- ☐ Good
- ☐ Fair
- ☐ Below Average
- ☐ Poor

What did you like MOST about this product? ______________________

What did you like LEAST about this product? ______________________

Please describe any problems you may have encountered with installing or using this demo: ______________________

How do you use this book (entertainment, education, etc.)? ______________________

Did you enjoy the approach of this book? ______________________

What is your level of computer expertise?

- ☐ New
- ☐ Dabbler
- ☐ Hacker
- ☐ Power User
- ☐ Programmer
- ☐ Experienced professional

What is the primary use for your PC?? ______________________

Is there any program or subject you would like to see The Waite Group cover in a similar approach? ______________________

Please describe your computer hardware:

Computer ______________ Hard disk ______________

5.25" disk drives ______________ 3.5" disk drives ______________

Video card ______________ Monitor ______________

Printer ______________ Peripherals ______________

Where did you buy this book?

- ☐ Bookstore (name: ______________________)
- ☐ Discount store (name: ______________________)
- ☐ Computer store (name: ______________________)
- ☐ Catalog (name: ______________________)
- ☐ Direct from WGP
- ☐ Other ______________

What price did you pay for this book? ______________

What influenced your purchase of this book? ______________________

- ☐ Recommendation
- ☐ Advertisement
- ☐ Magazine review
- ☐ Store display
- ☐ Mailing
- ☐ Book's format
- ☐ Reputation of The Waite Group
- ☐ Topic

How many computer books do you buy each year? ______________

How many other Waite Group books do you own? ______________

What is your favorite Waite Group book? ______________________

Additional comments? ______________________

☐ **Check here for a free Waite Group Press catalog**

PLACE
STAMP
HERE

Waite Group Press, Inc.
Attention: *Nanotechnology Playhouse*
200 Tamal Plaza
Corte Madera, CA 94925

FOLD HERE